THIS BOOK IS DEDICATED
TO JESSICA WHO WILL BE
ALWAYS 12 YEARS OLD

MY LORDS, LADIES
AND GENTLEMEN

WE ARE ASLEEP. OUR LIFE IS LIKE A DREAM.
BUT IN OUR BETTER HOURS WE WAKE UP,
JUST ENOUGH TO REALISE THAT WE ARE
DREAMING.
                LUDWIG WITTGENSTEIN
                —A LETTER

AT THE BEHEST OF THE
PROPRIETORS IT GIVES ME
GREAT PLEASURE TO
PRESENT:

THE TEN DIMENSIONAL

A DIGITAL FANTASY IN THE SPIRIT OF LEWIS CARROLL

JAN ARUNDELL
TED ARUNDELL

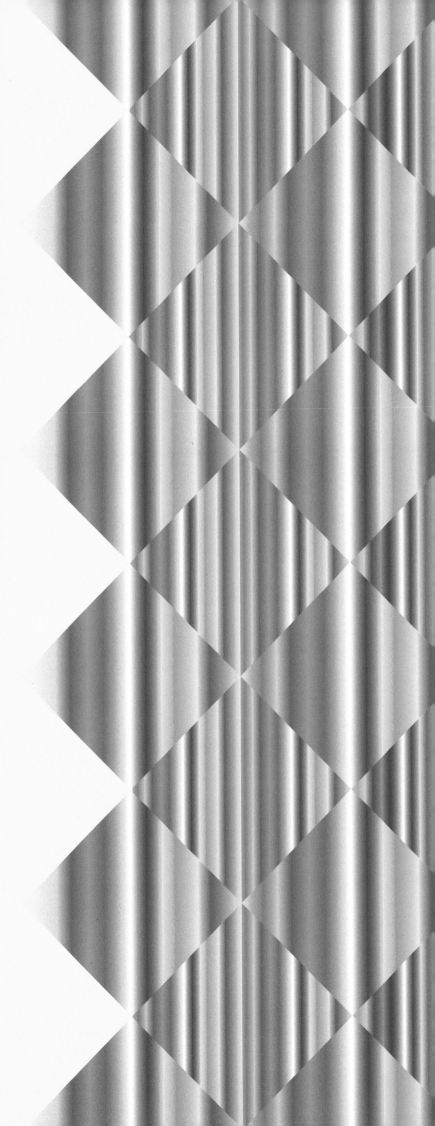

ACKNOWLEDGEMENT

As you linger over the images in this book a part here or there or an entire image may bring to mind the work of the following artists:

GAUGUIN HOCKNEY NICHOLSON MUCHA DE FEURE
TANGUY TENNIEL ROSSETTI ESCHER VASARELY

THANKS ARE DUE TO:

ANNIE WHITAKER for correcting my appalling spelling.

KATE HAINES for showing me where to put the commas.

BRIAN SURETIES for righting my more glaring grammatical howlers.

Ted Arundell

THIS BOOK HAS BEEN PRODUCED
BY THE CO-OPERATIVE EFFORT OF
BARCO GRAPHICS, JARROLD BOOK
PRINTING AND TASMAN STUDIO.

THE SPECTACULAR QUALITY OF
THE PAGE THAT YOU ARE READING,
THE SHARP DEFINITION OF THE
LETTER FORMS, THE RICH COLOUR
OF THE BACKGROUND HAVE BEEN
ACHIEVED USING FOUR COLOUR
PROCESS PRINTING, BACKED BY
STATE-OF-THE-ART DESIGN AND
PRE-PRESS TECHNOLOGIES.

ORIGINATION

GRAPHIC DESIGN	Jan & Ted Arundell
TEXT	Ted Arundell
APPLICATIONS	Graphics & Page Layout: Macromedia FreeHand
HARDWARE	Computer: Apple Power Macintosh 7100/66/24/250

PREPRESS BARCO Graphics

APPLICATIONS	File Translation: BARCO Graphics TRANSSCRIPT
	Editing: BARCO Graphics PAGELINE
	Imposition: BARCO Graphics IMPOSE!
	Ripping: BARCO Graphics FASTRIP/B
	Screening: BARCO Graphics MONET SCREENS (stochastic)
HARDWARE	Workstation: BG-2500
	Monitor: BARCO Reference Calibrator
	Imagesetter: BARCO Graphics MEGASETTER

PRINTING Jarrold Book Printing

The faithful reproduction of minute details and depth of colour in this book has been achieved with MONET SCREENS, the latest stochastic (quasi random) dot patterns from BARCO Graphics.

ORGANISATION

CONSULTANT	Brigette Scandrett	PROJECT CONTROL	Chris Arundell

All product names are trade marks or registered trade marks of their respective owners

INTRODUCTION

He was lost. He tried to read the sign but it was covered by a clump of seaweed which oozed a vile, salty liquid.

"Yuk!"

He clutched his nose and wanted to be off, but he stayed; he really was in desperate need of directions. The seaweed was easy to remove, making sense of the sign was not so easy.

TO THE CHAPTERROCKS 769 WORDS

He puzzled over the matter until an idea came to him. Tut-tutting, he drew from his pocket a miniature laser wand which he used to burn off the first two letters of the last word. Then, on the pulverised spots, he beamed in a **Y** and an **A**.

TO THE CHAPTERROCKS 769 YARDS

He stuffed the wand back into his pocket and began to pace out 769 yards while muttering, "These remnants from the past...these stone-age measurements...why can't people get up-to-date...use the metric system...listen to the latest, greatest superrock soundquakes...ditch the period crap and repro junk zapping their senses, and swing into hi-tech living...

And what the heck is this?"

His way was blocked by a notice-board announcing the auction of a 16th Century Manor. Hurriedly he read the details, then switched his gaze beyond the board to the Manor itself, a rambling building of dark wood, pebble glass, weathered brick and stone, a prize example of 'period crap'.

11

With his thoughts scrambling after the ideal setup for the good life, he strode along a driveway leading to a great window which rose at the centre of the Manor.

As he drew closer he saw that the window was caked with the grime of neglect.

From his pocket he drew a tangle of tissues and used it to create a spy-hole of clear glass. With his eye widened to match the size of the spy-hole, he peered into the room beyond.

"Now that's more like it!"

The admiration in his voice was as bright as the incandescent glow coming from a BARCO Graphics WYSIWYG Holographic Projection that filled the centre of a 'rococo' (repro. junk?) interior.

WORDS NOT YARDS CONTINUE FURTHER

The message flashed on and off across the room and wiped the shine from his voice as he spat out, "Just how screwed up can you get? Whoever's punched out that garbage can stuff his words with yards, I'm going back the way I came!"

With a flourish that would have done credit to a courtier, he spun on his heels and took off.

"There are some real schizos around. Screwing up words with yards is what happens when you stick white hot technology into a clapped-out relic like that old dump. Why don't people smarten up?...Are we living in the present or hiding in the past?...What a crazy mixed-up world!"

So he bumbled on, with nonsense oozing out of nonsense, until his irate tone lost its edge and another sound could be heard.

It came from the sea. He slowed down, cocked an ear to fix the direction, then came to a stop. His intention to return the way he had come, weakened at the happy thought of sailboards skimming over glistening surf, warm sand, superreality amusement arcades and lazy teas taken on the pier to the strains of Colonel Bogey (not exactly one of the 'latest greatest superrock soundquakes'), played by a Brashbrassband.

"Now here's a chance to do something real sharp and zippy!
Show those hacks what it's all about!
Bring in a bit of the old Post-Postmodern with...

    a gym
    a barbie
    a jacuzzi
    a games room
    a swimming pool
    a hi-tech bowling alley
    a couple of squash courts and
    a hideaway all wired for sound and superreality...

Yes, I reckon I could tell those Proprietors, whoever they are, a thing or two about living in the modern world!"

In hot pursuit of his blissful vision, he crossed a stretch of lawn to a gate leading out of the grounds and onto a track that twisted for a kilometre or so. In time the country air gave way to sea breezes and he found himself on a cliff overlooking, not a thriving seaside resort, but a murky beach 'cleansed' by a grey and angry sea. Smothering a sense of disappointment at having to settle for a dreary work of nature, when he had been hankering for a glitzy work of man, he told himself that it couldn't be helped. Life's like that and he might as well make the most of it.

He stood to attention, drew in a deep breath of salty air and..."Not that stuff again"...emptied his lungs in one sharp burst, looked about him for the cause of his hasty exhalation and saw a great pile of seaweed.

"Pooh, how it pongs!"

He prodded the pile with his toe.

"Yuk!Yuk!Yuk!" he exclaimed, pinching his nose against the waves of sickening stench that rose up in defence of the disturbed weed.

Feeling something hard, he thrust his foot deeper into the soggy goo and winkled out a number of rocks. Still using his foot, he scraped away a wet, spongy covering to reveal that on each of the rocks was chiselled an inscription.

He studied the rocks to learn their meaning. The words were plain enough, yet taken all together, what did they mean? He was bothered by a feeling that they were important, but important in what way? One thing seemed sure, whatever their meaning, they had nothing to do with him.

1 THE UNDERWATER BIOSCOPE SHOW
2 THE PASSAGE
3 A GENERAL DORMAN
4 INTO BATTLE
5 A 20TH CENT. QUESTIONER
6 LIFE DOWN THE MANHOLE
7 THE FOOL AND THE JESTER
8 THE YESMAN
9 HE HAS NO GREAT TALENT
10 GOBBLEDYGOOK
11 KOOGY DEL BBOG
12 THE VENDING MACHINE
13 A VERY PROMISING PM
14 THE CABINET
15 THE GENERAL CONFESSES
16 THE PUPPETEER'S DREAM
17 KOOGY STOPS READING
18 WHAT HAPPENED?

SUPERREALITY = VIRTUAL REALITY + VIRTUAL INFINITE MEMORY

He was drowning. In trying to solve the riddle of the rocks he had been careless and had fallen into the angry sea. Normally he would have kept his head above the waves, but these waters were vicious and the struggle to survive had quickly drained his strength.

Down he sank. Away from the turbulent surface he entered a dream-like state in which his eyes sucked in every gleam of underwater light. His scrambled mind, desperate to beat sense into the light falling upon his retinae, saw a silver screen on which was projected a mess of images. His body, succumbing to his hallucination, settled into a sitting position as though ready for a Bioscope Show.

ROLL UP

FOR THE GREATEST, THE MOST EXCITING, THE MOST SPLENDIFEROUS SHOW ON EARTH, BY KIND PERMISSION OF THE PROPRIETORS, AND AT E-N-O-R-M-O-U-S EXPENSE, I AM PRIVILEGED TO PRESENT FOR YOUR EXPRESS ENJOYMENT, A NEVER BEFORE SEEN, ONCE AND ONLY, NEVER TO BE REPEATED, WORLD PREMIERE AND FINALE PRESENTATION OF:

ROLL UP
ROLL UP
ROLL UP

ROLL UP
ROLL UP
ROLL UP

THE WONDER WATER BIOSCOPE SHOW

EXCITING

1

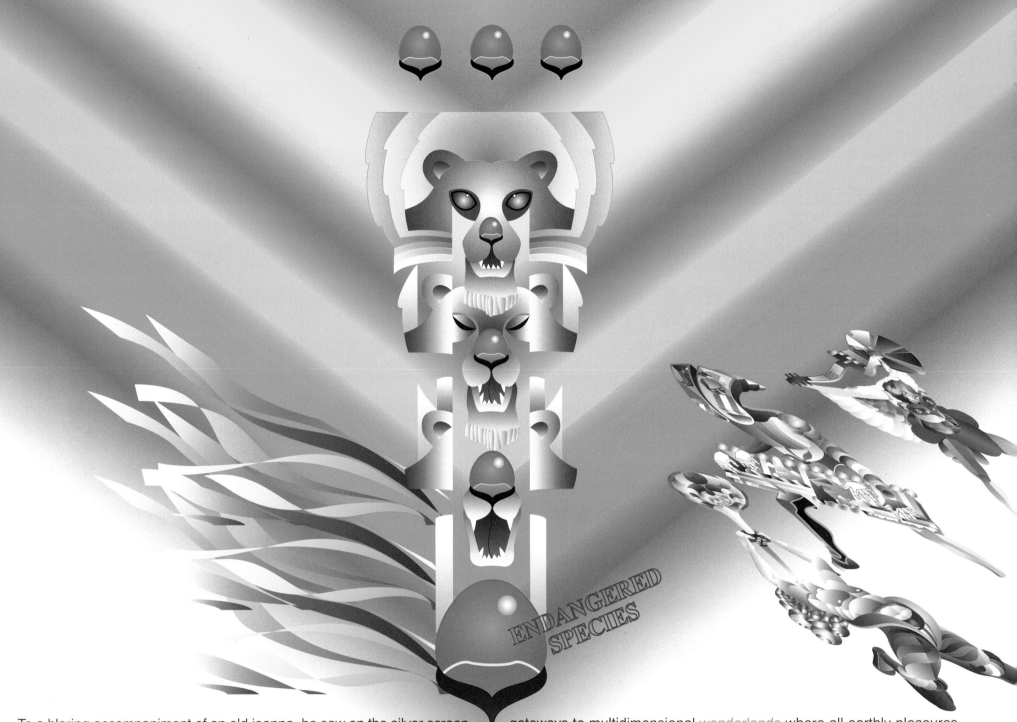

ENDANGERED SPECIES

To a blaring accompaniment of an old joanna, he saw on the silver screen, of all things, a sneeze, a thunderous sneeze, a lion's sneeze, a sneeze that soared above the jangle of the ivory keys.

And of course, a nose, a lion's nose, a big nose, a nose that was growing bigger by the second. And for a while a pair of glowing eyes, a gaping mouth and the other bits and pieces that go to make up a lion's head.

For a while that is, until the nose completely filled the screen, no longer silver, but radiating colours so intense that the whole underwater scene became saturated with shimmering rainbow hues. Just the ticket for an intergalactic soundquake performed by the Cyclotronic Proton Smashers. And there they were, in all their glory, as a mind-pounding opener to the raging images that followed. Images of superrealities within superrealities;

gateways to multidimensional wonderlands where all earthly pleasures pale beside electropleasure, which in turn pales beside nuclipleasure, which in turn pales beside the pleasure that would infuse your whole being, if only you would buy an Andromeda Ripple Crunchy Chocy Bar with Scrumptiously Toasted Mouth-Watering Tropicana Betelnuts. All you have to do is put your money in the chocolate coated, green, white and gold vending machine.

What? You have no money?

Goodbye electropleasure! Goodbye nuclipleasure! Goodbye everything!

His hallucination came to an end in silence and in darkness.

SOUNDQUAKE   SUPERREALITY

THE PASAGE 2

He was floundering in an underground

pool and choking up water fit to burst. He felt terrible, and terrified that he might sink again beneath the waves. For once, his star shone upon him, for the current that had almost destroyed him, changed direction and lifted him up. Now in its dying phase, it nudged him onto a flat area of rock where he lay until he felt strong enough to sit up.

The rock was part of the floor of a passage which was lit dimly by the glow from a scattering of neon lights from...what? Could he believe his eyes...pictures? Was he in a picture gallery? Whatever. He dragged himself to his feet, stood uncertainly for a moment, fought to master his shaking body, focused his gaze along the passage and took an agonising step into...unconsciousness.

But he must get up. Even the darkness must not deter him. He rose to his feet and groped about to find that he was in a room...a tomb? There was a door, but it was locked. The cord that secured his cloak came undone. He stopped to tie it. A sliver of light so distracted him that he left the knot loosely formed.

He felt his way over to the light and discovered that it came from a crack in the wall. He put an eye to it but saw nothing but blinding light. His hand made contact with the wall which seemed to give at his touch, inviting him to push. He pushed, and the wall around the crack began to move. Frantically, he tore at the loose bricks, forcing them into the space beyond.

PICTURE

DARKNESS

GALLERY

FURNESS

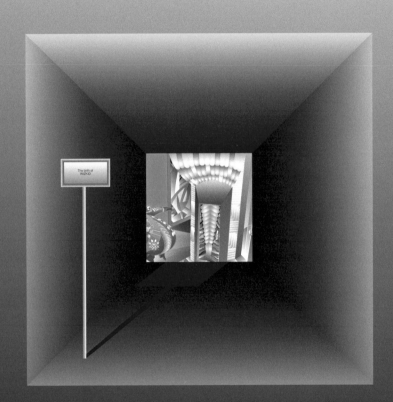

The light that streamed through the opening dazzled him, like the brilliance of fire seen through the open door of a furnace. An overwhelming desire to get out took hold of him. With all his strength he forced a way into the breach. The cord dangling from his cloak became entangled with the brickwork; for a moment the loose knot held; he tugged...the cord came away and fell to the floor.

When he had scrambled clear of the rubble, he had the feeling that he was in a...long place...a corridor...a gallery? He was not sure. The brightness dazzled him. He could just make out a figure. Were those medals glinting in the light? Were they pinned to the uniform of a soldier? Was the hazy image...a major...a colonel...a general? One thing was sure, its lips were moving. They uttered no sound, yet their message was plain to read:

WIZKID

Then Wizkid regained consciousness.

GENERAL DORMAN

INFO

Bully for youthful vigour. Any one seeing Wizkid striding forth would not have believed that not so very long ago he had fainted from sheer exhaustion. Now, with the underground passage behind him, he had arrived by way of a number of adventures (not included in the book to keep down production costs) at another passage, or more properly, a corridor. Not the all too common dreary affair lined with uninviting doors that promise nothing worthwhile beyond, but rather an elongated Aladdin's cave of wondrous delights. Light shone from here, there, everywhere, especially from a mirrored ceiling that reflected the dazzle and sparkle of it all.

The corridor was studded with doors of such variety and splendour that they seemed to vie with each other for Wizkid's attention. If only he would turn this or that handle and give a little push, just a *little* push, into an exciting world of endless adventure.

ADVENTURES GALORE.

Suddenly he stopped. The door in front of him had commanded him to do so. At least that was his impression. It was modelled in the form of a triumphal arch of such military style that Wizkid fancied he could see the proud ranks of La Grande Armée marching through it. Martial music filled the air, and he could hear the distant sound of gunfire mingled with cries of jubilation, confusion and despair.

Goodness knows where his fancy would have led him had the spell not been shattered by a Blitzkrieg.

"A General! He must be at least a General!" blurted Wizkid, as the door burst open to reveal a magnificent looking man in the most elaborate be-medalled uniform Wizkid had ever seen.

In fine military style, the General marched into the middle of the corridor.

Perhaps 'marched' is not quite the right word, for the General had no legs; no legs at all. Where the jackboots should have been, there lurked a tank to which he was attached by means of a universal bio-mechanical coupling (a very useful device for a general, enabling him to screw into any piece of military hardware that takes his fancy).

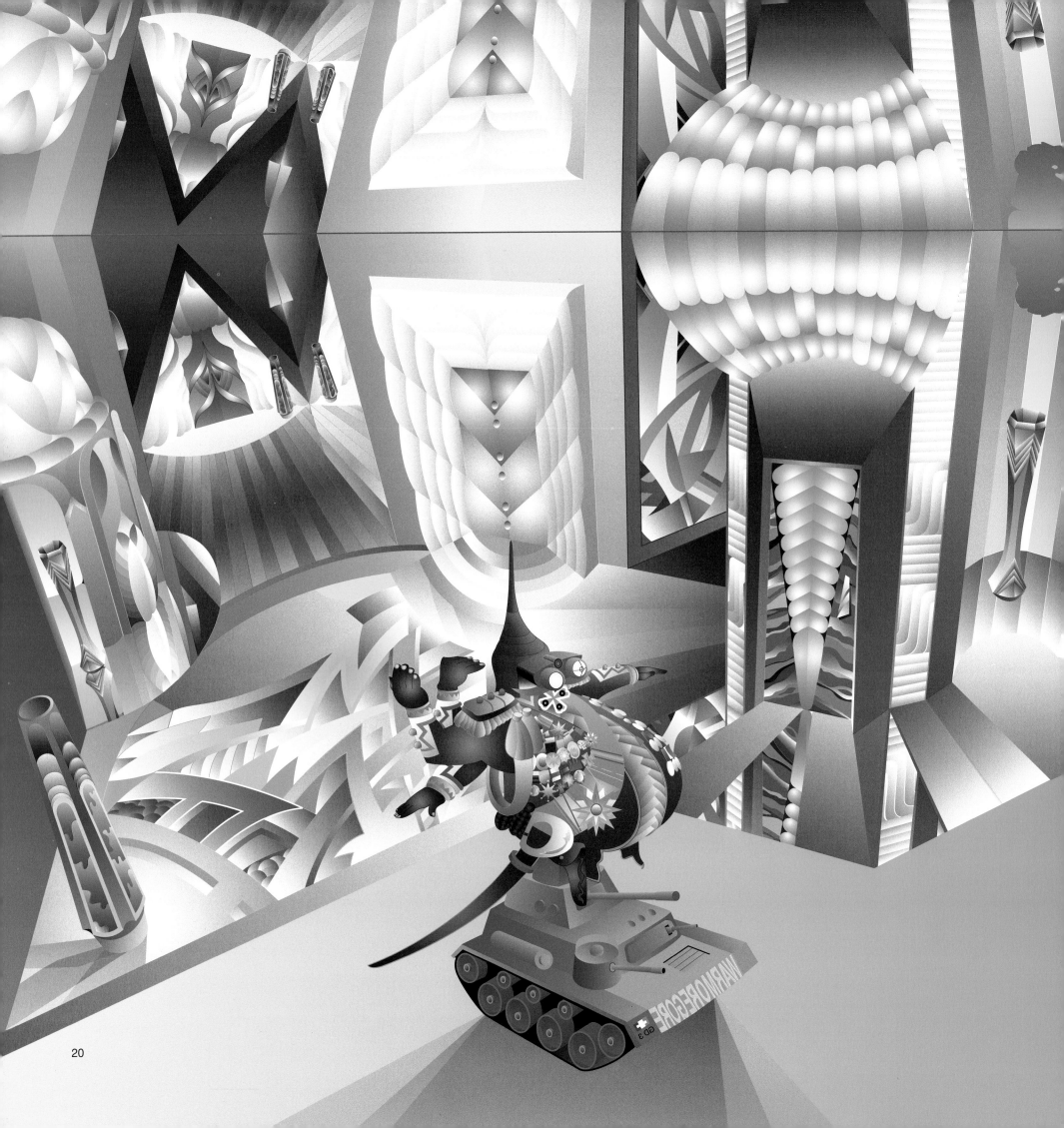

LADIES AND GENTLEMEN, AT THE BEHEST OF THE PROPRIETORS AND ON BEHALF OF THE WHOLE CIVILISED WORLD, I MUST PROTEST MOST STRONGLY CONCERNING THE UNPARDONABLE EXTRAVAGANCE, MONUMENTAL PROFLIGACY AND DOWNRIGHT SQUANDERING OF PUBLIC MONIES UPON THE ACQUISITION OF DIABOLICAL WEAPONS TO WHICH CERTAIN GENTLEMEN ARE ADDICTED. THEREFORE, AS A MAN OF THE THEATRE, MAY I MAKE A SUGGESTION, ALBEIT A MODEST SUGGESTION OF MY OWN...

TURN THE JUNK INTO STAGE SETS

Before the tank had time to settle on its tracks, the General began waving his arms about like a policeman directing traffic along a high street.

"Move along there, move along!"

"Excuse me."

"Move along there," bawled the General, ignoring Wizkid in spite of the fact that they stood almost eyeball to eyeball.

"EXCUSE ME."

The General's arms dropped to his sides and he frowned deeply. "You should not interrupt people at work," he said petulantly. "It's most inefficient."

"Look, if you really want to be efficient, you can tell me where I can find Nilrem, the Project Controller."

"Don't be ridiculous! That's the signpost's job. How do you think it would feel if I took over its work?"

"You must be seeing things. There is no signpost."

"And there never will be, if I start telling people where to go."

After a pause, in which the General seemed to have thought better of his objection to giving directions, he said, "I would go through those two." As he spoke, he pointed in the direction of two nearby doors.

"You're not talking to identical twins you know. I can't go through two doors, not at the same time anyway."

"Wrong again!"

"OK. So tell me why I should go through two doors when I only want to see one person."

"For the same reason that you put on two shoes to go for one walk, or listen to one song with two ears," said the General with contempt. "Besides," he continued, warming to the subject, "why do you think he is called both Nilrem and the Project Controller? So that he can be in two places at once, of course."

It seemed to Wizkid that maybe somewhere in a remote corner of the Universe, due to some peculiarity of this, that, or the other, the General's words may well convey a devastating logic not enjoyed by the folks on Earth. Anyway he'd better do something quickly as the General's arms were beginning to move again.

"General... !" blurted Wizkid, putting out a hand to hinder the hyperactive arm, "...is your uniform machine washable?"

"Actually," proclaimed the General, beaming from epaulette to epaulette, "actually," he continued, with his chest swelling to twice its normal size, "I'm not really a General you know. It's very kind of you to say so and I'm most flattered, but..." and at this point his smile vanished, to be replaced by such a gloomy expression that the medals on his chest seemed to lose their shine, "...I'm only a Dorman. A kind of General Dorman, I suppose, but still only a Dorman."

"Don't you mean *Door*man?" corrected Wizkid.

"Wrong again," snorted the Ex-General, "when I say Dorman I mean Dorman; short for Corridorman. If I were a Doorman, I'd be in a doorway, but I'm not, I'm in a corridor...there is a difference you know. For example, being a Dorman is sadder than being a Doorman."

The Dorman fell silent. Wizkid waited, hoping he would soon learn the reason for the Dorman's curious manoeuvring. As the latter was in no hurry to continue the offensive, Wizkid went into the attack.

"Don't keep me in suspense; blind me with science; why is being a Dorman sadder than being a Doorman?"

The Dorman burst into tears and his chest was soon heaving so vigorously that the medals began to jingle. It was not until red streaks appeared on the Dorman's glorious uniform that he paused in his crying, only to start up again even more violently when he realised that the red streaks were caused by his medals rusting from the tears streaming down his face and chest.

"I knew those medals were only silver painted," sobbed the Dorman, now over the worst of his ordeal. "You see, being a Dorman gets sadder and sadder all the time."

"You'll probably find the shells in the tank are duds too," commented Wizkid dryly.

"Wrong again. If you think you are so clever, tell me, why does being a Dorman get sadder all the time?"

Faced with this challenge, a challenge of awesome complexity, Wizkid tried to imagine himself in that remote corner of the Universe where the General Dorman's utterances meant more than cold rice pudding. If only

he could get there, all would be made plain. Unhappily, between him and the great revelation, yawned a battle zone, in which aircraft were being blasted out of the sky, buildings were collapsing like ninepins, armies were being ground to dust, yet he found himself replying with mind-boggling wit to the cold rice pudding.

"Because your cold rice pudding is rusty...I mean...your medals are rusty?"

"Wrong again," rejoined the Dorman, beginning to sob once more. "For one thing," he continued through his sobs, "he only has one 'O' instead of two in his title, and for another, there is no such thing as a Dorman. You cannot get any sadder than a Nosuchthing."

As if to prove the point, his body sank into the tank, popped out again and then went through the most alarming distortions to end up looking a bit like a Signpost, and a bit like a General, and a bit like a Dorman, and a bit like the picture opposite.

The above transformations will be familiar to 22nd Century readers. For the benefit of our 20th and 21st Century readers, it should be explained that such happenings are the mark of mischievous dimension hackers. They hack their way into the Ten Dimensional Maze, and plant viruses and other exotica that wreak havoc well beyond the system in which they are placed. As we shall see shortly, the Maze is quite capable of radiating cranky events of its own without help from outside.

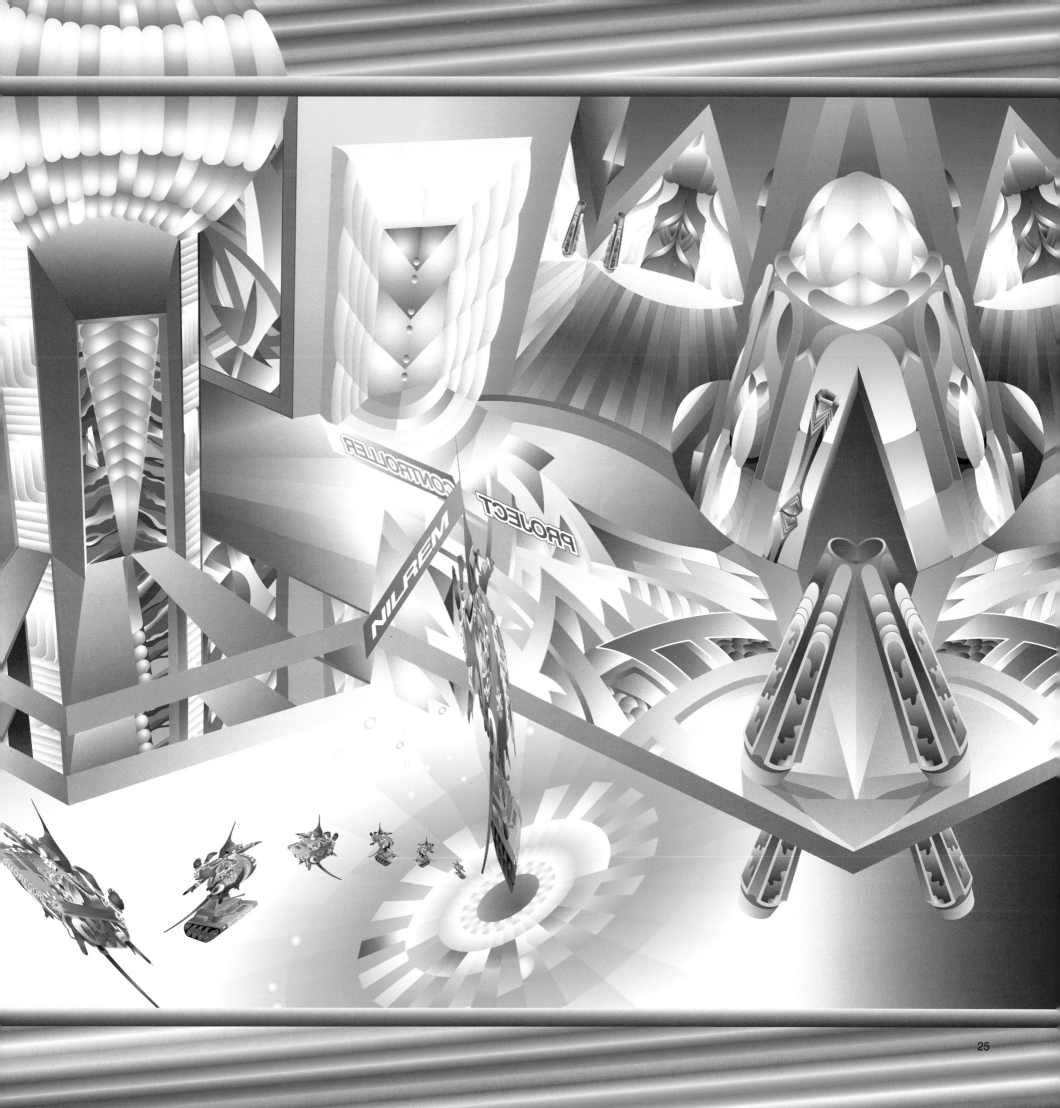

4 INTO BATTLE

NILREM said one arm of the signpost.

PROJECT CONTROLLER said the other.

"I'm wasting time," said Wizkid.

"And time wastes you," said a voice.

Wizkid looked sharply both ways along the corridor. He was thoroughly foxed for he could see no one.

"Now I'm hearing voices, would you believe? What I need is a holiday, get away from it all, a spell with Electropleasure, or even better, with Nuclipleasure."

He felt something brush against his legs, and looking down he actually saw a fox. A Fox? Well, more exactly an animated hologram of a Fox, a Desert Fox. The animal made its way to the first of the two doors, nudged it open and was gone.

Before Wizkid had recovered from the encounter he heard a noise behind him. He pivoted round to face another wonder of holographic technology. A fierce Desert Rat was snapping and snarling en route for the second of the two doors.

"Into battle, don't dawdle, there's little enough time to waste," screeched the voice.

The door swung open and the Rat, too, was gone.

Then the bombardment began. The bombs were feathers. The feathers came from a bird. The bird was a Cocky. The Cocky squawked and flapped its wings so much that the whole corridor was aflutter and filled with nerve-shattering sound.

"Prepare for battle...put 'em to rout," it squawked as it flew back and forth along the corridor.

"Cut 'em down...**EXTERMINATE**," and other blood curdling war-cries filled the air before the Cocky was reduced to silence by

PUT 'EM TO ROUT

EXTERMINATE

the silent advance of a squadron of razzle-dazzle, kooky-kolored barrage balloons. They bobbed prettily down the corridor, until every square centimetre of the ceiling was covered with a bouncing, throbbing mass of op-arty gorgeousness. The Cocky was not impressed by the lively addition to the décor. It gave one last squawk of annoyance at the intrusion into its airspace and landed on top of a column of hats, where it collapsed into a heap of ruffled feathers.

The hats towered on top of what looked like a blown-up fragment of dishevelled onion, but which, as it was walking backwards and pulling a loaded cart, just had to be animal rather than vegetable.

Where the creature had come from, or who or what it was, Wizkid had no idea. He decided to follow it, but before he could do so, it opened one of the many doors through which it, its cart, the Cocky and Wizkid's hope of making a new acquaintance, disappeared.

The devouring door showed signs of having once possessed a regal splendour. Now it was in an advanced state of decay. Peeling red white and blue paint hung on those parts of the woodwork that were still able to provide a hold, while the floor on either side was littered with the remains of silver and gold leaf that had long ago dignified the surrounding panelling.

He pushed open the door, and was about to enter the room beyond when his eye caught the gleam of an object lying in the débris. He scooped it up, and brushing off some fragments, saw that it was a gold plate.

It's new and very shiny," thought Wizkid, "so it couldn't have been there for long."

He turned it over and over in his hands hoping to discover where it had come from. Instead, he succeeded only in making himself blink, as shafts of deadly light flashed into his eyes. He held the plate at arm's length. It did the trick. The flashing stopped and he saw that it was inscribed with the following commands:

FIX BAYONETS! PREPARE TO CHARGE!

With the plate firmly in his grasp, irradiating all before him, Wizkid charged through the open door, telling himself that it must have fallen from the cart, and that he must catch up with its owner, to return the dazzling prize.

A 2000 CENTURY QUESTIONER 5

Wizkid burst into the room and ran slap into the enemy's barricade. It was defended by a man whose uniform consisted of a stone suit that seemed to have been carved out for someone at least a foot taller. The barricade was a counter that divided the battlefield into two halves. On one side of the counter the man guarded piles of dust-laden paper and on the other there were a number of benches on which sat rows of silent people. Above it all swirled a fog of cigarette smoke.

Of the cart and its owner there was no trace.

For a moment Wizkid dithered. Were all the people waiting for something? Should he wait his turn? The idea of joining the sombre crowd did not appeal to him, yet he did not want to cause offence.

"Next!" bellowed the Man in the tall suit.

Stirring themselves, the people on the benches looked about them in alarm.

"Next! You standing there, you'll do." The Man beckoned Wizkid to approach the counter. As he did so, a great sigh of relief came from the crowded benches.

"Your number?" he demanded, stabbing his index finger in the direction of the dazzling gold plate in Wizkid's hand.

Hesitating, Wizkid tendered the radiant object, only to have it torn from his grasp.

"Name?" spat out the Questioner as he conjured a form from beneath the counter.

"Wizkid."

"No, not your nickname, your proper name."

"Alis...Alistaire." stuttered Wizkid.

"Alice," confirmed the Questioner.

"No, ALISTAIRE, not Alice. I'm not a GIRL! " objected Wizkid vehemently.

"I won't know that until I've asked you which sex you are. Anyway we have to establish that you were born, before dealing with whether you are male or female."

"Place of birth?"

"Unknown," answered Wizkid.

"UN--K--N--O--WN," repeated the Questioner as he wrote it down. "That's strange, I've never heard of that place before," he said, looking enquiringly at what he had written.

"No, no, you don't understand, UNKNOWN isn't the name of a real place...there's no such place."

"Don't be ridiculous! It's beautifully written here in black and white...plain as a pikestaff...of course it's a real place."

Domicile?" demanded the Questioner sharply, giving Wizkid no chance to argue the point further.

"What?" asked Wizkid, looking puzzled.

"What', is no way to address a person...a person's address is most important in determining his standing in the world."

Wizkid looked blankly at the Questioner who responded by disappearing into the shadows at the back of the room. A little later he reappeared clutching a computer print-out. He beamed at Wizkid.

"Well, well, well, you are a dark horse, a most distinguished address," he gushed as he produced a deeply upholstered chair from behind the counter and placed it next to Wizkid. "I hope that you will forgive me if I continue to ask you questions. It must be very demeaning for a person like yourself, but the wheels must go round, as they say."

Wizkid sat in the chair saying nothing, as he struggled inwardly to adjust to the Questioner's change of attitude.

"Are you male or female?" the Questioner asked unctuously.

"Male, what else?"

"Oh, very good sir," enthused the Questioner and he carefully inserted the word 'male', in the correct place on the form.

"Your nationality, sir?"

Wizkid's reply caused the Questioner to lean across the counter and hug him so hard that all the breath was squeezed out of his body. Then he grabbed Wizkid by the hand and pumped it vigorously.

"Allow me to congratulate you. You have the honour of belonging to the greatest little country in the world."

The Questioner's behaviour caused a change in the people sitting on the benches. From within the folds of their clothing they brought out flags, multicoloured streamers, rattles and the like, which they waved frantically to the accompaniment of loud cheers.

The razzmataz disturbed the piles of paper and soon a dust cloud filled the room. The patriotic cheers changed to choking, coughing and tears. The waving stopped. The party was over. The dust began to settle and the patriots settled back on the benches.

"What is your occupation, Sir?" With his eyes still watery, the Questioner returned to his task as though nothing had happened.

"Apprentice W..." began Wizkid, wiping his tears.

"Apprentice, only an APPRENTICE?" interrupted the Questioner. "You mean to sit there...you do realise you should not be sitting on that chair? It's against regulation number $E = MC^2$

"Don't be daft, that's Einstein's energy/matter equation," said Wizkid, "you sure you've got the right glasses on?"

In reply the chair vanished from under him and he found himself sitting on the floor.

"Married?" asked the Questioner, bending over the counter and peering down at Wizkid.

"Married?" queried Wizkid, looking up at the Questioner in amazement.

"Married," repeated the Questioner, writing the word on the form.

"No, no, no, I'm not married," blurted out Wizkid.

"You ought to be ashamed of yourself trying to pass off as unmarried. I feel downright sorry for your poor wife. And what about the children?" As he spoke he inserted '4 children', on the form.

Again the Questioner leaned across the counter and peered down at Wizkid.

"What sort of man are you? Rolling around on the ground whilst your poor wife and howling children are looking everywhere for you. Why don't you pull yourself together and be your age?" He ran his eyes quickly over the form to check if there was any mention of Wizkid's age and seeing none, he added, "Whatever it is".

"What a lot of crap you've been giving me. My age won't be found on your idiot form and as for having a wife and kids, you've got to be joking!"

"In an agency," proclaimed the Questioner.

"In a what?"

"Your age could be found in an agency."

"I don't see the connection," objected Wizkid, getting up from the floor and brushing dust from his clothes.

"Of course you don't. That's because you're not a gent. For a while I believed you were a gent but only because I was off-form. Now that I'm more in-formed I can see exactly what you are."

"What am I?" asked Wizkid, challengingly.

Looking at the top of the form he replied, "You're No. 13."

"That's a terrible thing to say."

"Quite right," agreed the Questioner. "I think it's awful to treat numbers as though they were just people. After all, a number has a very special character of its own. Mind you, I've seen some very odd numbers in my line of work. But then again, I've come across some pretty natural ones too. They can sometimes be exceedingly complex and give one a hard time trying to understand them. So much so, that when I am asleep I often

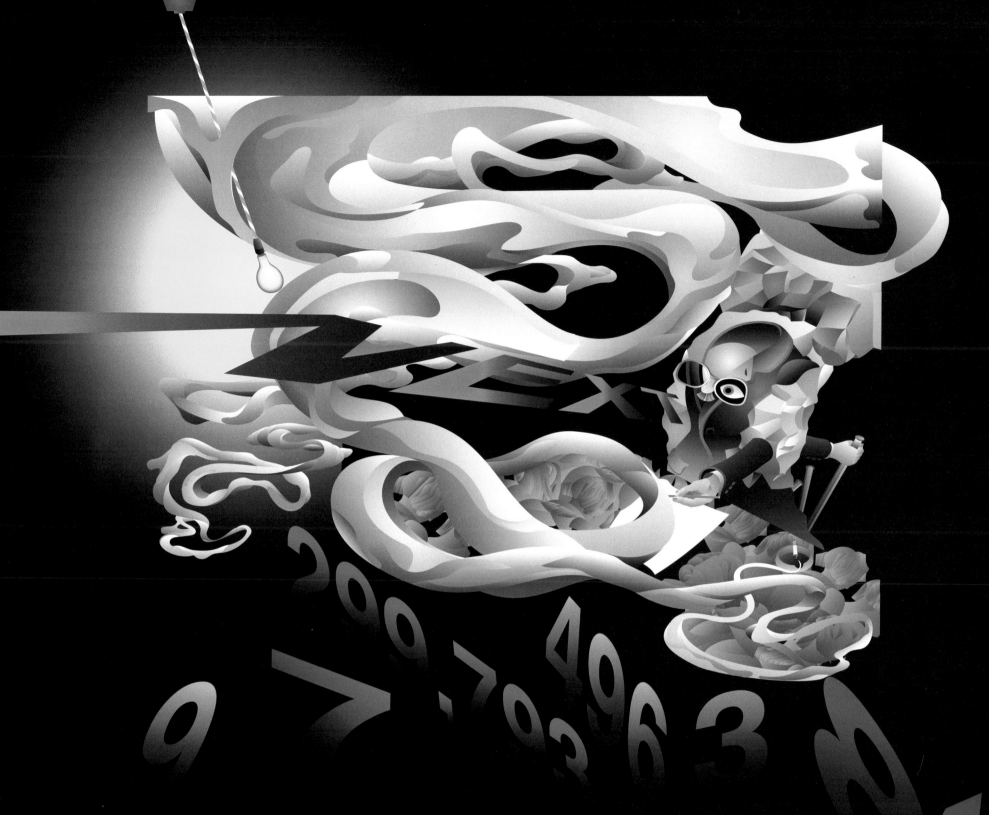

see imaginary numbers in my dreams, only to wake up to find that they are real numbers. Now and again, I encounter a perfect number - that's a beautiful experience..."

Wizkid listened as the Questioner drifted off to a universe of numbers. For him, Wizkid, the people sitting on the benches, the room and all that it contained, ceased to exist.

"...and negative numbers are so unresponsive that one often feels like taking them by their serifs and giving them a good shaking. On the other hand, positive numbers conduct themselves with such dash and

determination that one cannot help but admire them..."

"Great!" murmured Wizkid, "Now's my chance."

Keeping a wary eye on the 20th Century Questioner, he gently slid the form over to his side of the counter.

"Gotcha!" he said softly, while inwardly congratulating himself on having breached the barricade to relieve the enemy of so personal a piece of intelligence.

6 LIFE DOWN THE MANHOLE

Wizkid was again in the corridor, and glad to be back on neutral territory. But something had changed, although he could not quite put his finger on it. Finger? Digit? Number?

"Yes, that's it! The doors have numbers!''

The first door, made in the shape of a number one, was numbered, 1. The next door was immense, and to Wizkid's surprise it was dignified not by a 2, but by a bold looking 3. Wizkid moved on quickly to its neighbour in the hope of finding a clue to this unusual way of numbering and discovered a door of circular construction with a large 4 at its centre. He passed from 7 and 11 to 18. Still no wiser, he began to walk faster. He moved so briskly that he barely had time to read the numbers, until something made him stop.

Sandwiched between 76 and 199, hung a double silver door from which radiated a golden light. Its brilliance warmed his skin. As he stood enjoying its effect, he noticed that if he moved his head ever so slightly, the number:

entered his field of vision.

Wizkid glanced at the form in his hand, and saw that it too was numbered:

"What the heck is this all about?

Before he had time to consider the puzzle properly, another puzzle came to his attention.

In a space set aside on the form, he saw that someone had entered his age. Wizkid touched the number with his index finger, only to withdraw it with a jerk. The ink was still wet. Not wishing to smudge it, he waved the form back and forth to dry the ink.

Draughtsman:	Dorman, do stop waving your arms about, you're causing no end of a draught in the cellar.
Coalman:	And while you're about it, keep an eye open for the Dustman.
Fireman:	Yes, tell him to hurry - we've been waiting long enough.
Lighterman:	Take care you don't fall down the manhole...I mean personhole.

For a moment Wizkid thought someone was having him on, until he saw there really was a manhole...I mean personhole. He pocketed the form and walked across to the opening, where he crouched down to look into the blackness.

Coalman:	Is the Dustman coming yet?
Fireman:	You can't come down here.
Draughtsman:	Yes! A Dorman's place is in a corridor.

Wizkid was about to tell the last speaker that he was not a Dorman, when the Coalman added hastily, "The same as a Coalman's place is with his coal," and he sighed.

"And a Fireman's place is at a fire," said the Fireman, heaving a deep sigh.

"And a Draughtsman's place is with his draughting," said the Draughtsman, who allowed his T-square to hang limply in his hand, as he heaved a very deep sigh.

"I suppose you are wondering why we're not more cheerful," continued the Draughtsman, after the sighing had stopped. "Well, it's like this..." and here he paused to take in air, "...I'm a Draughtsman and my friend over there is a Fireman and the man standing next to him is a Coalman and the man who is hiding is a Lighterman and the man who is not here is a Dustman... and that's the reason." After a moment's reflection the Draughtsman carried on, "And if that's not reason enough - which it is - then all I can say is, it is one reason too many." At this point the Coalman and the Fireman nodded their agreement so energetically that their hats fell off.

"What I say is, that if you have one too many of anything, then you should give it to someone who has one too few," said the Coalman, looking daggers at the Fireman who had picked up both hats.

"You are quite sure you're not a Dustman?" asked the Coalman, who was wrestling with the Fireman because the latter had refused to return his hat.

"Do I look like a Dustman?" retorted Wizkid.

The Coalman was now on his knees trying to free his hat from the Fireman's grasp, and at the same time bring his opponent to the floor.

"Are you an umpire then?"

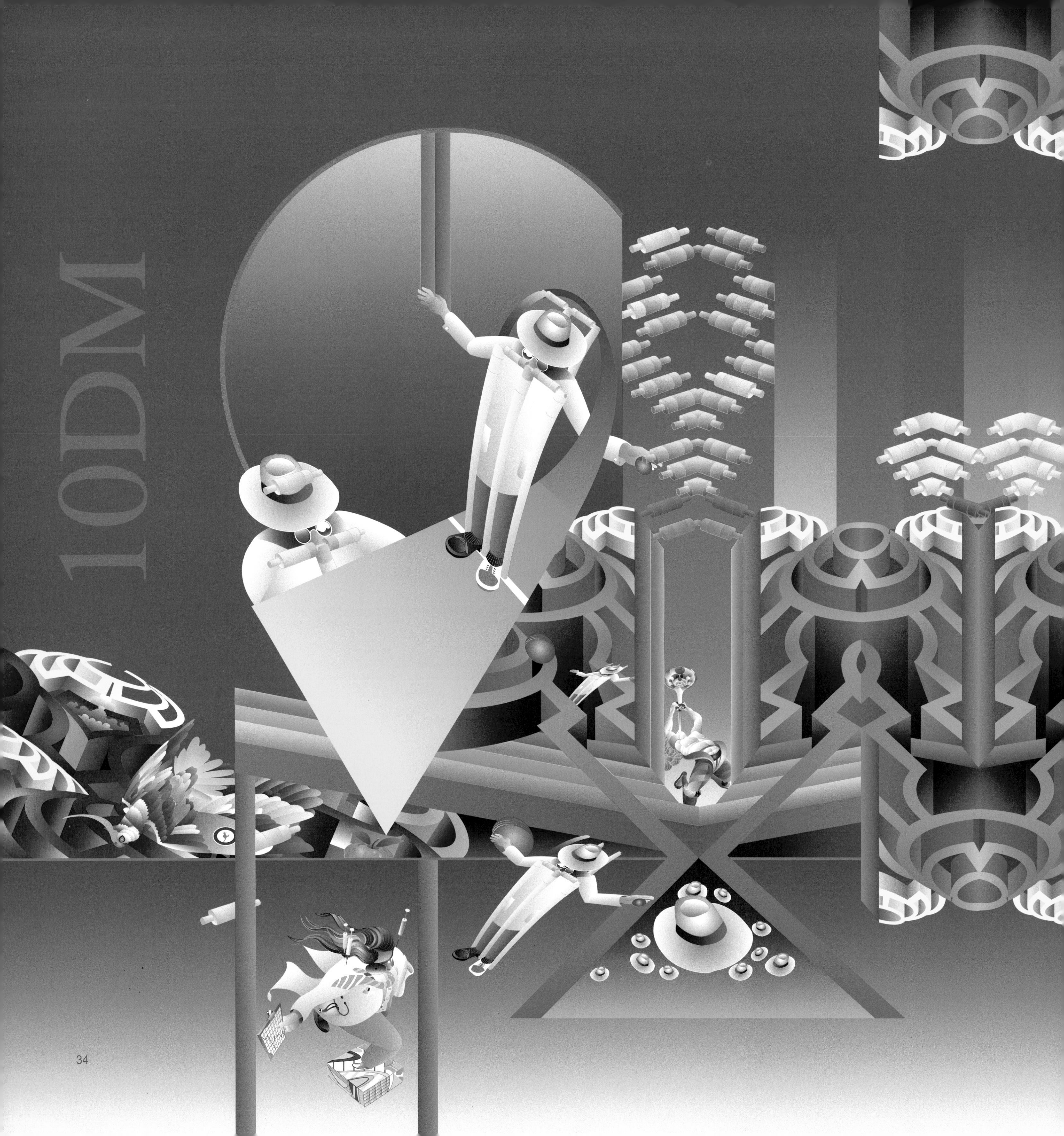
10DM

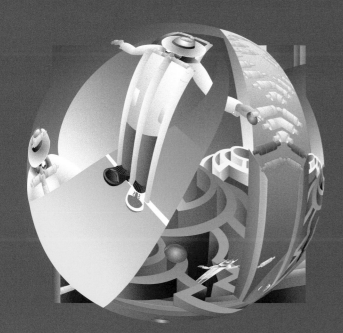

Before Wizkid could answer, the Fireman lost his balance and he and the Coalman fell into a heap. When they untangled themselves, Wizkid saw that each had a black eye.

"Are you by any chance a Medicalman?"

As he spoke the Coalman revealed that as well as possessing one black eye, he was dispossessed of one front tooth.

A VERY FAMOUS MAD HATTER

As everyone knows hatters were not just mad, they were stark raving mad. So, with a couple of mad hat owners on our hands, we thought we would include an illustration of a very famous Mad Hatter.

INFO

EXTINCT SPECIES

We could have illustrated an up to date model of a medicalman, but as this species has joined the Tasmanian Tiger along with 99% of the rest of the world's life forms, it is not possible. Medicine, like most other trades of the past, has been digitised. We could of course show you the hardware but as it consists of a box no more than 30cm x 30cm x 10cm, it would have been spectacularly unspectacular on its own. So instead we have illustrated a typical late 20th Century doctor scudding through one of the under-manned and overcrowded monumental hospitals before they were chunked into a space 30cm x 30cm x 10cm.

"Or a Hatter?" asked the Fireman, eyeing his battered hat that was now in the hands of the Coalman. During the scuffle each contestant had lost his hat to the other, and now they stood glowering madly at one another.

"I say, why don't you two blokes make it up and swap clothes?" suggested the Draughtsman.

"Wouldn't it be easier to exchange hats?"

"They've done that already and they are a darned sight less happy than they were and if they did it again they would be unlivable with and I for one would leave the cellar forthwith," replied the Draughtsman.

"I don't see why you should."

"You may be right or then again you may be wrong either way I shouldn't know whether it would be so or not because I shouldn't be here to find out unless of course when I came back you were to tell me if it were so or not in which case it would be as if I were here all the time."

The Draughtsman had drawn in more air than he needed to finish his speech. So as not to waste it he added, **"The Late 16th Century Manor was built by Sir Christopher Dog in the year MDLIVII from time to time thereafter it was extended and in no small degree abused in the year MMCLI it was put up for auction following the sale the Manor was renovated and subsequently became a museum since then its fabric and contents have been looked after in a way guaranteed to secure their preservation for the future with the..."** at which point his words trailed off because his breath was all used up.

While the Draughtsman had been prattling on, the Coalman, and the Fireman had agreed to swap clothes, but could not agree who should hand over which garment first.

"You are quite sure that you are not an umpire?" asked the Coalman looking hopefully at Wizkid.

"If he were you would have been sent off for pulling me to the ground," answered the Fireman sulkily.

"You may have a point there or then again you may not because if he were an umpire he may not have sent off the Coalman because you might have already been disqualified for picking up the Coalman's hat in the first place however if he had not disqualified you the Coalman should most certainly have been sent off for pulling you to the ground therefore if he is an umpire he is not on a busman's holiday," said the Draughtsman. He grinned at everyone because he had breathed in exactly the right amount of air needed to finish on the last word.

"No one could put it plainer than that," said

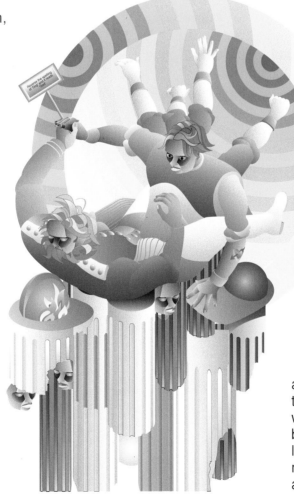

the Fireman to cover up his envy at not having thought of the argument himself.

"I don't agree," said the Coalman who had not been listening very closely to what was being said, but disagreed with the Fireman on principle.

They fell silent and the Fireman scratched his head and looked intently at the ground.

"Suppose we take off our jackets and hand them to our young friend to swap around," suggested the Fireman, looking up at Wizkid.

"I don't agree," said the Coalman.

"Suppose you two blokes take off your jackets and hand them to our young friend to swap around," suggested the Draughtsman.

"I like that suggestion a lot better," said the Coalman.

The matter being settled the Coalman and the Fireman lost no time in removing their garments and handing them up to Wizkid who swapped them around and handed them back to their new owners.

Then the Draughtsman proposed that they exchanged trousers but the Coalman, who was shy, pretended that the cellar was too cold for him to uncover his legs. The Draughtsman got up from the floor and made his way to a corner of the cellar where Wizkid could just see the outline of an ancient boiler. He opened a squeaky little door in its side and waved his T-square back and forth in front of the opening.

"You're wasting your time. No amount of draught will bring the fire to life," said the Fireman, "at least not until the Coalman puts on some more coal."

"Flibbertigibbet," replied the Coalman, "it won't burn because the Dustman hasn't come to remove the dust."

"All it needs is for the Lighterman to put a light to it," opined the Draughtsman.

The last remark caused the Lighterman to protest (from a dark corner of the cellar), that just because he was timid that was no reason to put the blame on him. Nobody would give an inch. Voices were raised and the argument became so heated that Wizkid was unable to suffer it any longer. He got up from his crouching position beside the manhole...I mean personhole...I really mean wormhole and turned towards the double silver door.

THE FOOL AND THE 7

The conviction came to him that beyond the silver doors something pleasant awaited him, and for a while at least, he would experience a kind of joy. Slowly he extended his arm and pushed. The doors parted at his touch to reveal the interior of a vast chamber.

The walls of the chamber rose to an immense height and from its loftiness fell cascades of shimmering shrink-resistant polyester fabrics which broke upon the floor in a boiling mass of iridescent colour. A sea of stain-repellent Nylon carpets stretched between walls covered with exotic melamine laminates. Here and there were eruptions of dark green plastic foliage that provided a sumptuous setting for the searing brilliance of banks of artificial flowers. The air was heavy with an aromatic scent that beguiled the nose, whilst to entrance the ear, a melodious chorus of recorded bird song accompanied a gentle refrain that came from a Copland BRUNO-60 programmable polyphonic synthesizer.

At the centre of all this splendour, sat a beautiful girl.

She was dressing a number of puppets that bore a close resemblance to the occupants of the cellar. The two that looked like the Coalman and the Fireman were receiving special attention, as the girl switched the clothes from one to the other.

She was so deeply absorbed in her task, that Wizkid had time to enjoy the delightful picture she made, sitting amongst the puppets with her skirt rippling over the carpet and forming an island of shimmering whiteness around her.

When she had finished the dressing, she took up the strings and with a flick of her wrists the puppets sprang to life. Wizkid was soon lost in wonder at the skill of the Puppeteer, as each of her charges recreated the role that its human counterpart had played down the manhole...I mean personhole...I really mean wormhole. The performance was so realistic

that Wizkid felt compelled to mime his part to the very end, after which, his role in the drama having ceased, he became its audience.

The chamber echoed with his clapping and gusty cries of admiration.

The sudden realisation that she had an audience, coupled with the unrestrained display of admiration, so affected the Puppeteer that for a moment she was quite put out. To cover her confusion she assured Wizkid that there was really very little to it, and that with a little practice he could do as well, and most likely a great deal better.

His look told her that he remained unconvinced and that his admiration remained undiminished, so to change the subject she asked him if he had come to see her holographic recording of the winners of the Intergalactic Rock-Around-the-Universe Contest, and did he know that the latest holographic technology was so good that it was impossible to tell their holographic images apart from the real thing, and that some of the performers had no real counterpart anyway, as they were of course themselves fanciful products of the mannequineans' art.

INFO

THE MANNEQUINEANS' ART

Mannequineans use holography to produce active copies of the human body. At least that was the original idea. Lately their work has developed into an art form that uses whimsical distortions to give dash and excitement to their creations. So successful have they become, that on some Dyson spheres it is fashionable to use nanotechnology to create similar whimsies on real human and humanoid bodies.

NANOTECHNOLOGY

Teeny-weeny assemblers assemble even teeny-weenier atoms to build or rebuild everything from the teeny-weeniest objects to toothpicks, bollards, trans-superspace transporters, planetary systems, galaxies, you, me, any darned thing that can be thought of and many more that would be hard to imagine.

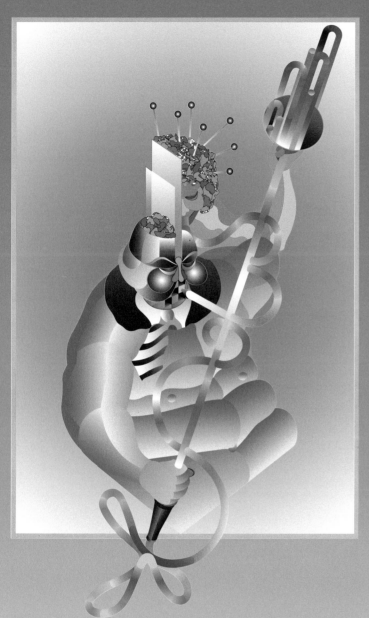

"You'll enjoy this," the Puppeteer said, fingering a brooch pinned to her lapel.

She glanced aloft. Wizkid's gaze followed hers and it seemed to him that the high ceiling of the chamber rose even higher. Then, from deep in space, descended a chunk of showbiz hardware. All aglow it was; vibrant with colour and sound; the sound of champions; winners of the Rock-Around-the-Universe Contest; the SUPERROCKETS from Downunder doing their thing, taking SUPERROCK into the future, P O U N D I N G!

And the accompanying pyrotechnics in 1...2...3...4...5...6...7...all good children go to heaven...7 dimensions, creating ecstasy in cyberspace; priming the grey matter for the devouring music of the Superrockets.

"Well, yeah, they're really something, but not what I'm after," was Wizkid's sober comment after the performance had run its dazzling course.

He was more impressed than he let on. He considered himself a Cyclotronic Proton Smashers' fan for they were THE GREATEST!

"What are you after then?"

"I'm trying to track down Nilrem, the Project Controller."

"That's a difficult one. Maybe the Jester or the Fool could help you?"

"Where do they hang out?"

"Follow me," said the Puppeteer, leading him by the arm.

She guided him to some steps leading down to a sunken floor covered with embroidered cushions, in the midst of which reclined the Jester and the Fool.

"But they are only puppets!"

The Puppeteer seemed hurt by his unthinking comment, but nevertheless she pulled him onto the cushions and said softly, "You must wait."

It was so peaceful sitting there beside her that he soon began to feel drowsy. He lay resting for a while, then, through the veil of approaching slumber, he heard a distant voice:

I said to the King, 'Yes?' and he said, 'No'.
I asked him, 'Why?' and he told me to go.
I told the Chamberlain he could and he said he couldn't.
I asked, 'May I?' and he said, 'You shouldn't.'

I said, 'Please!', to the Equerry and he said to me, 'So..?'
I told him to try and he said, 'You must know...'
I asked him, 'What?' and he said to me, 'That...'
I said, 'You must tell me,' but he turned me down flat.

I asked for the Guard's mercy and he said, 'Maybe.'
I asked for his pity and he said, 'I'll see.'
I cried, 'Help!' to the Cook and she said, 'Don't fret'.
I said, 'Immediately?' and she said, 'Not yet.'

I called to the Page, 'Morning!' and he called, 'G'day!'.
I said to him, 'Raining!' and he said, 'Hooray!'
I asked, 'Please assist me,' and he asked, 'At what?'
I said to him pleading, 'This so and so of a computer
has bombed again and I need someone to help
me put the darned thing right!'

As Wizkid came out of his slumber, a second voice joined the first; and there they were, as large as life...the Jester and the Fool.

"The situation does not seem very hopeful," said the Jester.

"On, but it is...," said the Fool, very gloomily, "... it's very hopeful indeed. It's years since there has been as much hope around as there is at present - it's so depressing!"

Wizkid had seldom seen a more unhappy looking creature. Indeed, the weight of the Fool's sorrow seemed to add substance to his head for it drooped listlessly between his hunched up legs.

"There's more and more hope being used up by the minute. Everyone is using so much of the stuff, it's so depressing!" The Fool moaned on until his moans became groans and his groans lapsed into silence.

All the while the Jester had been trying to cheer up his friend by making faces, standing on his head, juggling cushions and pulling out of his pocket an endless stream of wallabies, rabbits, field mice, dishes of rice pudding (steaming hot), corkscrews and reject fine art.

The Jester's antics must have had some effect because the Fool opened his mouth to speak, groaned, sucked in some air, groaned again, sucked in some more air and said, "The more hope there is for them the less hope there is for me. It's so depressing!"

The Jester was busily standing the fine art, cushions, wallabies, rabbits field mice, rice puddings (no longer steaming) and corkscrews, one on top of the other in an attempt to build a tower. His progress was hampered by the rice pudding, a particularly tacky variety of rice pudding, which he tried in vain to remove from the items to which it had stuck. The performance had no effect upon the Fool other than to make him grumble "It's so depressing."

Undeterred, the Jester carried on with his attempt to build a tower. Instead of wiping off the rice pudding, he used it to stick the items together Everything was going nicely until the wallabies took into their heads to jump down and chase the field mice in circles.

Each time one of the wallabies passed the Fool it would brush lightly against his legs, causing him to giggle.

"I had hoped they would not do that," said the Jester, trying to catch the creatures as they hopped past.

"It will run out one day, you know," advised the Fool, giggling in between every second word, "you can't go on using up hope for ever. If only people were more hopeless, the more hopeful things would be. It's SO DEPRESSING!"

The Fool tried hard to look sorrowful but could only manage it for a second now and again, because the wallabies were brushing against him so relentlessly, he was being tickled almost nonstop. After a while the effort became too much for him and he stopped looking sorrowful altogether.

Eventually the Jester succeeded in catching the animals. To stop them running off again, he placed a dollop of rice pudding (now quite cold), on each of their noses. They were so busy trying to lick it off, that he was able to do as he liked with them.

Meanwhile the Fool was feeling put out, because being sorrowful had always kept him nicely occupied and now he had nothing to do. To stop himself from fidgeting, he resumed talking to the Jester.

"The Page Boy wouldn't help to fix the computer because he hoped to get some tarts from the Cook, who wouldn't help as she did not care to annoy the Guard whom she hoped to marry. The Guard wouldn't help as he did not wish to upset the Equerry from whom he hoped to borrow a horse."

At this point the Fool had to raise his voice, because the Jester had climbed to the top of a huge pile of cushions in his effort to build the tower to a great height.

"The Equerry wouldn't help as he had no desire to annoy the Chamberlain whom he hoped would lend him some money and the Chamberlain would not help because he did not wish to upset the King."

As he could think of nothing more to say, the Fool started to fidget and he did not stop until the Jester, shouting from on high, asked why the King had refused to help.

"Because he cannot relate to the technology," shouted the Fool.

The King had studied under the scholastics in the University of Paris during the 13th Century, where he had been surprised to learn that the Earth is not flat but a sphere. He was still finding it hard to accept the idea although his Chamberlain reckoned he would soon be ready to be told that the Earth goes round the Sun and not vice versa.

"Perhaps the PM could be asked," suggested the Jester, who began to sway unsteadily at the top of the tower.

"He is hopelessly hopeful," replied the Jester, "and anyway, all he would do is promise to do something about it and that's the kiss of death to any project."

For a while they talked in this way. Eventually the Jester suggested that Nilrem was the person to fix the computer.

Until the mention of the Controller's name, Wizkid had been so absorbed by what was going on that it hadn't occurred to him to speak. Now he tried to open his mouth but to his horror, he found that he could not do so. Stark-naked terror gripped him as he tried to move his arms but this too was impossible. Even his eyes were locked firmly in position. He could see the Fool perfectly, but nothing else.

"But no one has seen the Controller for ages."

"Well then, ask the apprentice where he is," proposed the Jester.

Wizkid, in a state of blind panic, only half heard what was being said.

"But it's only a puppet!" exclaimed the Fool, looking contemptuously at Wizkid, who desperately wanted to protest but as hard as he tried, he could not utter a single word.

He was under a spell, a devilish spell. What could he do? He wanted to scream but he could not. He could make no sound, yet sound there was.

Spell breaking sound!

The sound of champions!

THE SUPERROCKETS!

Mind filling, stretching, penetrating sound!

Penetrating the mind, the chamber, the Manor, out into the World and back again!

Back to Wizkid and, 1...2...3...4...5...6...7, all good children go to heaven.

1 The Fool went to pick up Wizkid.

2 The Jester fell from the tower.

3 The tower came tumbling down.

4 The Fool and the Jester turned back into puppets.

5 Wizkid shook the puppets.

6 One of the puppets burst.

7 Stuffing spilled onto the cushions and into Wizkid's eyes.

Blinking uncontrollably, Wizkid thought he saw the fieldmice and wallabies scurrying off with the corkscrews between their teeth. Then he felt a movement at his side. He turned to see the Puppeteer nursing the Jester. She was murmuring soothingly to him. With great seriousness she explained to Wizkid that while he had been asleep, the puppet had fallen and hurt himself and that she was having no end of trouble consoling him.

"He doesn't always moan, you know. Why, only a moment ago he was telling me about his conversation with the Fool. It seems that your friend the Controller, hasn't been seen for a long time."

She rocked the puppet in her arms whilst singing a lullaby about a tower built of cushions, wallabies, rabbits, fieldmice, rice pudding, corkscrews and reject fine art. After a while the Puppeteer declared that the Jester had stopped moaning, so she propped him and his companion against some cushions. She blew them a goodbye kiss, smiled and winked at Wizkid, "I am sorry they couldn't help you, but don't worry, I've lots more friends."

THE YESMAN

8

"Yes, we'll go to see the Yesman," declared the Puppeteer.

"The Yesman?" queried Wizkid.

"Yes, the Yesman."

"Yes."

"I see you have the knack already," said the Puppeteer, pleased with Wizkid's response. "Whatever you do, always agree with him."

"Why?"

"Because he's a very important person."

Wizkid didn't like the sound of it but he didn't argue with her. She really was a stunner.

He was led away from the sunken floor through a nearby door into a Post-Postmodern Quadrangle at the centre of which stood the Maze.

INFO

The Ten Dimensional Maze is an invention of the 22nd. Century. Its design is based on a ropey 20th. Century shenanigan called Superstring Theory (actually the theory should have popped up a lot later but the Proprietors are keen Superstring buffs so they shoved it into the 20th. Century even though it was clearly marked 21st. Century).

Like most good inventions the idea behind it is simple, i.e., when our everyday 4 spacetime dimensions were blown out of the Big Bang, 6 kinky dimensions were blown out too, all curled up tight and tiny, that is until it was discovered how they could be uncurled and stretched to form giant hoola-hoops. So, what the heck to do with them? Obvious. Place them concentrically, give them a little pat here and there, fill in the gaps with polymorphous supermatter and voila! You have...

THE TEN DIMENSIONAL MAZE

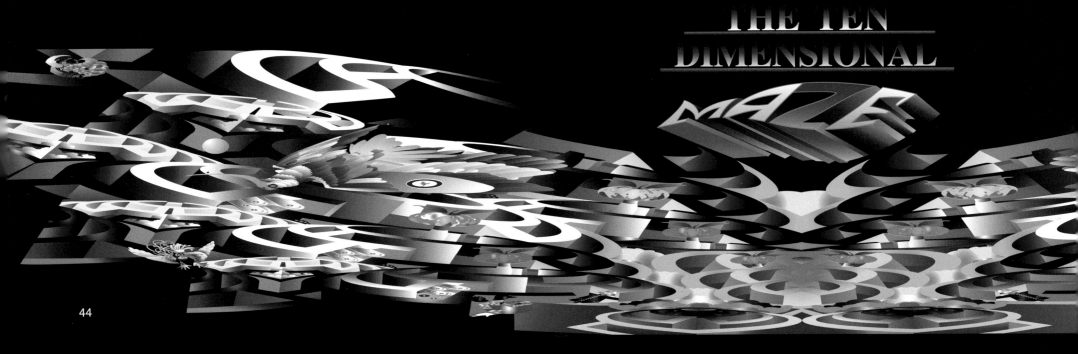

INFO

All very straight forward. Yes?...No! Out of the blue, all on its own, the crazy Maze has managed to attract a couple of stray time dimensions. The engineers have been working their socks off trying to discover where the strays have come from and whether or not they can be put to good use.

After spending 3 trillion yuan trying to solve the problem, one of the engineers was reported to have been overheard muttering through clenched teeth, "That double-crossing, two-timing, overgrown...of a Maze should be bulldozed, concreted over and privatised before it bankrupts the Exchequer."

The official view is that the project is going well and with another 3 trillion yuan grant, the maverick could be brought to heel.

Wizkid was given no time to dawdle. Relentlessly the Puppeteer dragged him towards the Maze. Once inside, she forced the pace even more. The intricate twisting and turning through a space irradiated by unfamiliar dimensions made Wizkid feel queasy.

Then sickly.

Then nauseated.

Then very, very dizzy.

Then he went crashing through an event horizon.

Then on into the maelstrom of a naked singularity.

Then powerful gravitational forces tore at his body, pulled his bones apart and shredded his mind (not unlike the sensation enjoyed attending a soundquake given by the Cyclotronic Proton Smashers).

Then his whole being slammed into a violent gear change...or that's how it seemed to him, for his head suddenly went boy-y-y-ing-g-g, instantly cleared and he could hear the Puppeteer saying,

"Sir, allow me to present ..."

"No, no, don't tell me, let me guess. Yes...I know...yes, it's a boy."

Wizkid looked in the direction of the speaker and he saw overlapping images of the Yesman (caused by the lingering effect of his cosmic mugging). The Yesman was dressed in a pink suit and wore a topee on his head. He sat upon a palanquin amidst many beautiful silks and other rich materials. The palanquin was supported by four bearers whom Wizkid recognised as the Coalman, the Fireman, the Draughtsman and the Lighterman.

When they saw Wizkid they became agitated and looked at one another woefully.

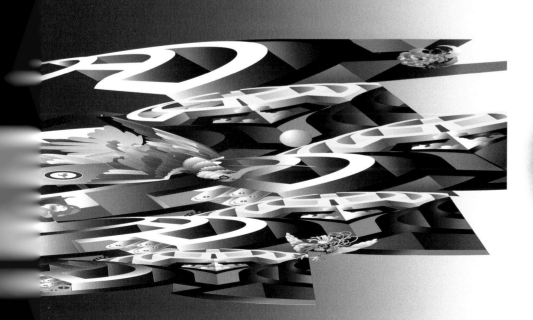

45

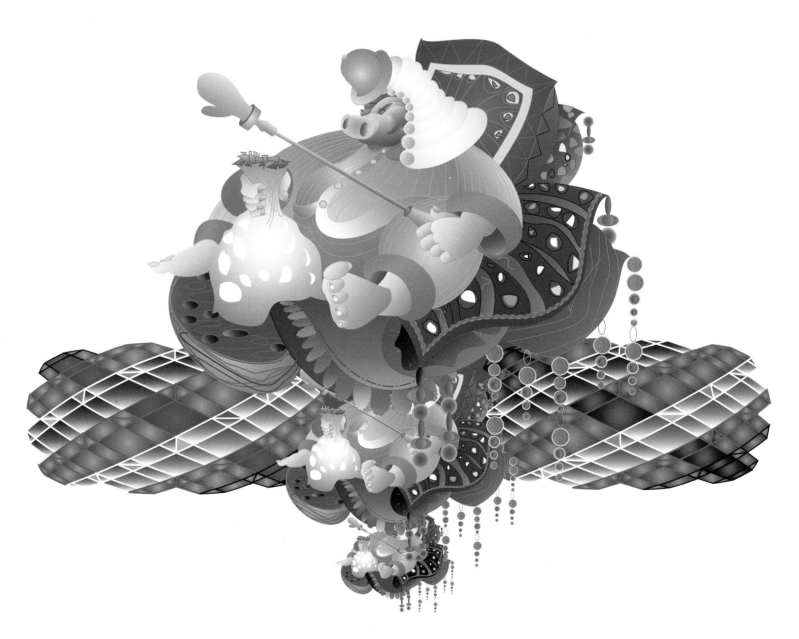

MISINFO?

Yes, I know, you are wondering how the four men could be supporting the Yesman if they were locked into an infinite loop. I must confess I don't know. However, the Ten Dimensional Maze does have a powerful recursive function which enables it to create effects that even its programmers and designers could not have foreseen.

On second thoughts, perhaps they were not in an infinite loop after all, but in a bounded loop. and we all know what that means.

"Whoa! Steady there, men!" commanded the Yesman and he gave each of them a wallop with a swatter which he carried in his left hand.

They recovered immediately and took to staring straight ahead.

"I can tell he's a boy because he is quite evidently all at sea," said the Yesman, beaming expectantly around the company. As no one responded to his witticism, he raised the swatter in the direction of the bearers who reacted with peals of humourless laughter. They went on for so long that the Yesman lost patience and brought his deadly weapon down upon their heads to make them stop.

Then he looked long and hard at Wizkid and demanded, "You do know the rule, Boy?"

"Yeah."

"How agreeable," beamed the Yesman, "have a gorgeous grenade," and he thrust a large white plastic bag in the direction of Wizkid.

"I prefer the ruby ones, so please leave those and take one of the others."

Wizkid did as he was bid.

"You have taken an un-ruby one, have you not?" asked the Yesman, leaning forward and peering anxiously at the object in Wizkid's hand.

Wizkid answered that he had, and as the grenade was rather sticky he thought he'd better eat it straight away. He was about to pop it into his mouth when the Yesman became alarmed.

" No! No! Don't do that!" he cried, in such a state of agitation that he was in danger of losing his balance.

Wizkid removed the grenade from his lips and the Yesman heaved a sigh of relief.

"Never eat today that which you can save for tomorrow," said the Yesman, his eyes glued to the grenade in Wizkid's hand.

"You've just made that up," blurted Wizkid.

"I'm very glad you agree with me," said the Yesman as he held the bag under Wizkid's nose, "put it in the bag and I'll save it for you for ... er ... for a rainy day."

Wizkid thought that the Yesman was really screwy, but did as he was directed just to keep the peace.

After Wizkid had returned the grenade the Yesman beamed happily.

"Did you by any chance, put a ruby grenade in the bag?"

"**Yes**, for pity's sake."

"How agreeable. They are my favourite kind, you understand," gloated the Yesman.

As there seemed to be no limit to the Yesman's self-satisfaction, Wizkid thought he would goad him by asking casually if the bearers were tired of standing and supporting such a heavy load.

"What a disagreeable question," responded the Yesman in great disgust. "Don't you agree, Girl?"

He looked challengingly at the Puppeteer, who replied with a reluctant, "Yes." When the Yesman looked away she winked at Wizkid.

"Most disagreeable. I refuse to discuss the subject further. Quite definitely!"

The Yesman tilted his nose in the air and made a great show of looking away from Wizkid. "Absolutely not. Never..." then after a pause, "I'm not at all heavy. It's just that I'm well built, a big bone structure, I think. Yes, that's it, a big bone structure!"

He looked at each of the party in turn and as no one showed any sign of agreeing with him he gave each of the bearers a wallop with the swatter. This made them nod their agreement so vigorously that he was forced to wallop them again to stop them from upsetting the palanquin.

"That's why I need lots of fat, juicy, gorgeous grenades, especially ruby ones. With a frame like mine I need a great many to keep me going. But that's enough about me. What about our friend here?" As he spoke he turned to look down benignly at Wizkid.

"Excuse me," said the Puppeteer, "he's looking for Nilrem, the Project Controller."

"Really...of course I have to look to my figure. I must keep myself fortified," said the Yesman and to show that he meant what he said he popped a grenade into his mouth. Then he began to make sucking noises that were extraordinary for a man although quite ordinary for a pig. The longer he sucked the more pig-like he sounded and the more pig-like he sounded the more pig-like he looked, or so it seemed to Wizkid.

"What are you staring at, Boy?"

"At a pigman."

"How agreeable. Yes, what charm the boy has." The Yesman pondered for a while and added. "Ye-e-es, I suppose I am a big man. Big hearted and with a generous spirit, wouldn't you say?"

"What's the difference?"

"There aren't any around here as most of our differences have been cleared up."

"What the heck does that mean?"

"Being of a greeny sort of hue they clash with the colour of my favourite grenades. At first I had the men white-wash them with Taubman's Vinyl Emulsion, external quality of course, but the rain cleaned it off before it had a chance to dry, so I had them all rounded up and locked away. Although, as they are rather slithery, the odd one escapes now and again. That's what this instrument is." He held up the swatter. "It's an odd slithery green difference swatter. Of course, it has other uses as well." He gave each of the bearers a wallop on the head by way of demonstration.

"As I was saying, the odd slithery green difference does escape, so if you are really interested in them and prepared to wait patiently, you can hear one from time to time."

"If they can be heard, then they can be seen too."

"Quite possibly, except that the more obvious differences seldom escape one, it is only the less obvious ones that get away."

"Then they wouldn't be heard either."

"You have a very good point there," said the Yesman, looking at the top of Wizkid's conical helmet. "If I were you I should keep it sharp. Who knows? You may be able to pin down the odd slithery green difference with it."

There was a note of finality in the Yesman's last comment so no one said anything further . The Yesman took advantage of the lull in the conversation to empty the contents of the bag into his lap. With delicacy, he held each of the grenades up to the light to admire its translucent brilliance. They were so beautiful that he purred and he purred over them. Between his purring he cocked an ear to hear the sound made by his 'jewels' as he dropped them back in the bag.

"I suppose you were wondering why I was listening to the sound of the grenades? "Well, I was experimenting to discover whether ruby and emerald grenades sound the same."

The Yesman looked importantly from the Puppeteer to Wizkid, each of whom was determined to show no sign of being impressed.

"Yes," he said, puffing himself out because he thought they were wonder-struck, "and my conclusion is," at this point he eyed the Puppeteer and Wizkid expectantly, "my conclusion is, that ruby grenades are more fanfaronade than emerald ones."

He continued looking at the two friends who were still unimpressed and decided that they were still too wonder-struck to speak.

"Of course, you wouldn't know what 'fanfaronade' means...it means that ruby grenades taste better than emerald ones."

"What about sapphire ones?" asked the Puppeteer, "Are sapphire ones as sweet as ruby ones?"

"What agreeable things you ask, my girl," said the Yesman, beaming. "Take a sapphire grenade."

"Thank you." The Puppeteer was awake to the Yesman's tricks so she lost no time in helping herself to a grenade. Even so, she was not fast enough. Before she could put it into her mouth, he directed her to hold the grenade over the opening of the bag.

"Now...when I say 'GO', let it drop into the bag...are you ready?...GO!" The instant the sapphire grenade had left the Puppeteer's hand he popped a ruby one into his mouth and quickly devoured it.

After a moment's consideration the Yesman declared that the ruby grenade tasted sweeter than the sapphire one sounded.

"But taste and sound are quite different," Wizkid complained peevishly.

"That was before our differences were cleared up," retorted the Yesman, "and you have broken the rule." He pointed a quivering finger at Wizkid who began to feel the vibrations of the Cyclotronic Proton Smashers' intergalactic soundquake starting up again.

"YOU HAVE BROKEN THE RULE!"

"I haven't broken the rule," objected Wizkid, struggling to form the words against the screwing effect of his spinning head.

"You have NOW," screeched the Yesman triumphantly, "and you must pay the penalty!"

"YOU HAVE BROKEN THE RULE!"

"YOU MUST SAY 'YES' TO HIM!"

"You must say 'yes' to him!"

The Puppeteer still held Wizkid by the hand but she was no longer tugging him along at break neck speed which was just as well, for he was fighting a fierce battle to capture a perch in her dimensions. She seemed unaware of the struggle that was raging beside her for she continued to chat about the Yesman...

...about him being a VIP...

Now he was in the throes of the final assault, a little more effort and he would make it.

...about the importance of always agreeing with him...

Eureka! He was on target. Now his mind had rejoined his body in the default dimensions.

...about the odd slithery green differences...

"You idiot. You screwball! If you are crazy enough to charge into the Ten Dimensional Maze unbriefed, then you deserve what you get," he chided himself.

...about the Yesman's pink suit.

"But wow! The Cyclotronic Proton Smashers' intergalactic soundquake is...is...there are no words to describe it."

...about his topee, the palanquin and, "You should see the way he wallops his bearers, the poor dears."

So she would have continued, had not her banter been drowned by a terrifying squealing.

Dozens of slithery green creatures, the like of which Wizkid had never seen before, were scurrying back and forth, creating a deafening din and spitting out life threatening clouds of poisonous fumes. The arrival of the two friends was not to the liking of the creatures for they raised their devilish heads high in the air, squealed a final squeal, then hurriedly removed themselves from the scene. If Wizkid had asked for something to concentrate his mind back in the default dimensions, he could have asked for nothing better.

"Oh, the poor Yesman!" exclaimed the Puppeteer in horror. She ran to where the creatures had been milling about and picked up a puppet that was all in tatters. "Or is it the Coalman or the Fireman...?"

Through tear-filled eyes she looked about her and saw the remains of two more puppets, then another and yet another. "You poor dears," she lamented as she went from one to the other of the puppets in an attempt to sort out which was which. "Whatever have those nasty slithery green differences done to you? We've arrived too late. Now as a **PENALTY**, we shall have to clear up your poor remains."

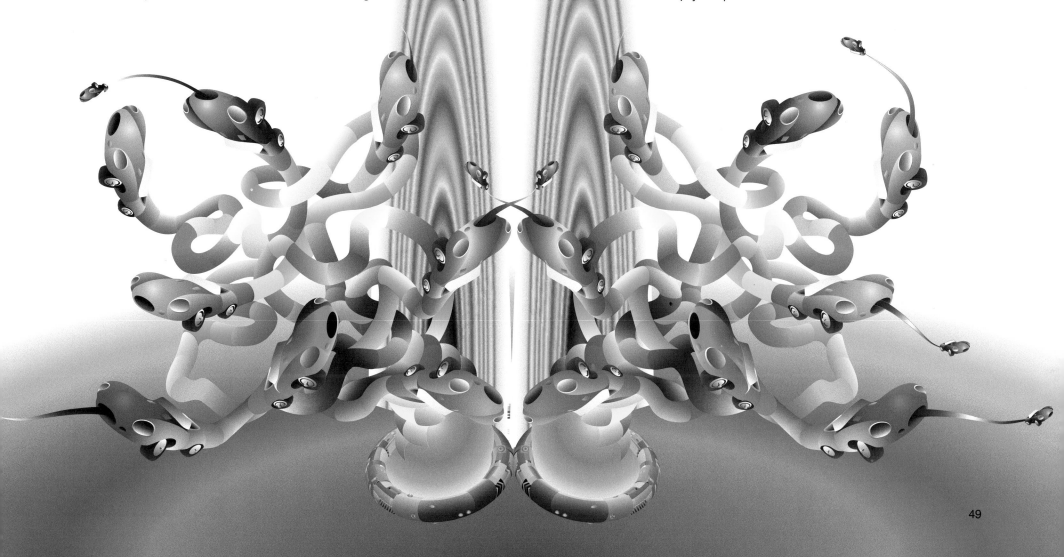

WARNING!

1   On no account should you enter the Maze unless you are thoroughly briefed about the peculiarities of its dimensional navigation.

2   You must leave your name with a responsible officer and inform him/her/it of your purpose in entering the Maze and the length of default time you intend to stay there.

3   Remember...rescue operations are time consuming and very expensive to mount.

INFO

No matter how good the gear, it will not perform at its best unless those who use it are tuned into its operation.

ATTEND THE LECTURES
ATTEND THE SEMINARS
ATTEND THE BRIEFINGS
READ THE MANUALS

And for Kaluza Klein's sake take the Ten Dimensional Control Möbius with you when entering the Maze, then you can really go, go, go! Go anywhere in the Universe and quite a few places beyond, in a manner of speaking.

TRAGEDY
DISASTER
CALAMITY

MY LORDS, LADIES AND GENTLEMEN, IT IS MY SAD AND SOMBRE TASK TO INFORM YOU, OUR READERS, THAT THE PROPRIETORS ARE IN LOW SPIRITS.

THEY WERE LOOKING FORWARD WITH BOUNDLESS ENTHUSIASM TO THE CONTINUATION OF THIS GREAT ADVENTURE INTO THE MANY WONDROUS REALMS ACCESSIBLE THROUGH THE MULTIDIMENSIONAL FACILITIES OF THE MAZE.

THEIR HIGH HOPES HAVE BEEN RUDELY DASHED BY WIZKID'S LAMENTABLE FAILURE TO UNDERGO PROPER INITIATION INTO ITS MYSTERIES. INSTEAD OF ACQUIRING THE COGNIZANCE THAT WOULD HAVE MADE HIM MASTER OF THE MAZE, HE IS DOOMED TO BE A VICTIM OF ITS UNREGULATED ENERGIES.

CALAMITY! TRAGEDY! DISASTER! WORDS DO NOT EXIST TO DESCRIBE THE IMMENSITY OF THE SETBACK. BUT WE MUST NOT FALTER. THE SHOW MUST GO ON!

ON WITH THE SHOW!

HE HAS NO GREAT TALENT

9

A breeze wafted through the place, carrying in its train a white patch. After entertaining them with a couple of somersaults, a spin around the big apple and other merry tricks (which caused the Puppeteer to dry the last of her tears), the patch came to rest against Wizkid. Peeling it from his body he saw that it was a large plastic bag and a sticky one at that. Thinking that it looked very like the Yesman's bag, he passed it to the Puppeteer, suggesting that it might be used to hold the puppets' remains.

"What a terrible thing to happen to the poor dears," she said, once the pieces were stowed away carefully and the bag placed against a hedge for safekeeping, "if only..."

TRUMP SNAP CRASH TWANG

He came 'through a hedge backwards', pulling a cart, his back decorated with a collage of buddleia, boronia, Banksia, bougainvillea, salamanders, Galàpagos finches, cicadas, bright green caterpillars and superstrings, signs of a fierce battle with the hedge. An awkward, shambling figure who, clear of one obstacle, was now tackling another. A branch, pulled from the undergrowth, had become entangled in the wheels of his cart, causing him to behave in a crazy fashion as he struggled to wrench it free.

 **Once the puppets' remains** had been gathered into a neat pile, the two friends felt free to consider their surroundings. Above them loomed a big apple. It was held aloft by a pillar of magnetically shaped plasma that rose out of a circle of lush grass. The oversized fruit made Wizkid salivate and the Puppeteer speculate that they must have arrived at one of the sub-centres of the Maze.

"Whoever he is, the poor bloke doesn't have much talent for freeing branches from wheels," observed Wizkid, grinning broadly. The Puppeteer nodded in agreement as they sat on the grass to await the arrival of the newcomer.

He gave a last desperate tug and the branch came free. The shock dislodged a Gobbledygook from a nest in the hedge. The bird showed its displeasure at being disturbed by beating the air with its wings and squawking wildly. Its protest made, it returned, much dishevelled, to its place of refuge.

"What an odd way to travel," noted the Puppeteer, once the newcomer had got going again. He was still shuffling backwards and pulling his vehicle along with him. As he did so, three of the many items that were piled on the cart fell to the ground. He retraced his steps, retrieved the fallen objects and resumed his backwards motion until, once again, something fell to the ground and once again he returned to pick it up.

"He has no great talent for making a secure load either," remarked the Puppeteer, as she watched the newcomer struggle to place a battered fireman's helmet, and an even more battered dustman's hat, in a safe spot on the piled up cart. "He'll never get here at this rate."

As the shambling figure drew slowly nearer, they were able to see that he wore layer upon layer of garments. "Rather like an onion," they remarked.

"And his hats!" exclaimed the Puppeteer. "How on earth does he manage to keep them all on his head, crashing through hedges the way he does?"

After much to-ing and fro-ing the newcomer was close enough for them to see plainly many of the things that were being transported with so much difficulty. The Puppeteer could not refrain from exclaiming, "What a peculiar collection of bits and bobs!"

In spite of the distance between them, the newcomer must have heard her, because he turned to see who had spoken and they found themselves gazing into the face of a gentle looking Drawde.

After dithering for a moment, he rallied, took a step back in their direction, saw some corkscrews and rusty medals lying in the grass, moved

forward to retrieve them, but was beaten to the task by the two friends.

While Wizkid and the Puppeteer gathered up the stray items, the Drawde managed to entangle the cart in a clump of turf.

The comedy that followed was more than the two friends could bear, as they struggled to restrain their laughter at the Drawde's struggle to restrain the turf. Their separate struggles ended in failure on the one part and success on the other, with the cart and its owner on the move once more and merriment all round.

This time the Drawde managed better, which caused Wizkid to remark, "If only things didn't get in his way, he'd get along as well as anyone."

When the Drawde had caught up with the two friends, he looked up coyly.

"Hello!" he ventured after a moment's hesitation.

"Hello!" they returned. Their cheery greeting made him smile sweetly, and with a little more assurance, he asked them whether they too, collected souvenirs. They shook their heads.

"Then you won't mind if I have my things back?"

When all the stray souvenirs had been returned to the Drawde, he made a clumsy attempt to arrange them on the cart, and in so doing dislodged a pair of binoculars and a T-square. As he bent to pick them up he said, "As you see I have no great talent for making a secure load."

"Then why have you collected so many souvenirs?" asked Wizkid.

The Drawde regarded him thoughtfully and replied, "I believe it is because I can't remember things." Then he paused and looked blankly at the cart. "But there may be other reasons I can't remember."

Wizkid was not much wiser, but not wanting to press the matter, asked him instead why he walked backwards.

"There are either three or four reasons why, but I can only recall one at present. Would you like to know what it is or would you rather wait until I remember the others as well?"

"Would that take long?" asked the Puppeteer anxiously.

"About three-quarters of a kilometre, I think," answered the Drawde after pondering for a moment. "But of course, that's only a guess."

Wizkid thought that he probably meant three-quarters of an hour or perhaps three-quarters of a day, but either way he did not want to wait, so he asked the Drawde to tell him what he could remember now.

"Reason Number 2, the one that I can recall, you understand, is that I walk backwards to keep an eye on where I've been."

"That's a bit unusual isn't it?" remarked Wizkid thinking, "He's all back to front."

"I really don't know about that, but what I do know, is that people usually ask me what it's like where I've been."

The effort of answering the questions made the Drawde a little tired so he said nothing more for a while. When he felt better, he told them that he was sure he had remembered reason Number 1, about a quarter of a kilometre ago and that if they cared to accompany him a little way, perhaps it would come to him again.

After they had been walking for a while, the Drawde said, "There you see, that's reason Number 1," as he pointed to a cage of some sort that had slipped from the cart, "I walk backwards so that I do not miss the souvenirs that fall to the ground."

Wizkid ran over to the object and brought it back.

The Drawde looked at it, scratched his head, stared at the cart, prodded at the things inside the cart, pulled out an odd slithery green difference swatter, held it out in front of him to see it better, looked at the souvenir that Wizkid had retrieved, and with a smile spreading across his face, exclaimed, "It's a Slithery Green Difference cage!"

He took it from Wizkid and examined it. "As you see, it's been broken open."

"How long have you had it?" asked Wizkid who was understandably curious about the souvenir.

"Well, let me think now..."

While he was pondering, the Drawde struggled to make a place for the cage on the cart.

"I suppose I got it about fifteen metres ago... on the other side of the hedge, I should think."

He succeeded in lodging the cage comfortably, but dislodged a nameplate with the words KOOGY DEL BBOG, inscribed on it.

"What's this for?" asked the Puppeteer, picking up the sign.

The Drawde came over all limp, flopped on the grass and said in a weak voice, "That's a rather strenuous question because I shall have to pull the cart for a kilometre or so before I can give you an answer."

The Puppeteer told him not to trouble himself.

He heaved a deep sigh of relief and lapsed into another of his weary silences.

This time it did not last for more than a moment because he saw something that made him brighten up. He rose to his feet and shuffled to where the Puppeteer had left the plastic bag. Motioning towards it, he asked her if

she would be kind enough to let him have one of her gorgeous grenades on account of the fact that he had a sweet tooth and anyway he had walked a long way that day and was in need of nourishment. "There aren't any left, if you'd..." Her voice trailed off in amazement as the Drawde bent down, took from the bag a bright red grenade and popped it into his mouth.

"You are very kind," he said as he sucked away with relish, "Its almost as good as an Andromeda Ripple Crunchy Chocy Bar with Scrumptiously Toasted Mouth-Watering Tropicana Betelnuts. I really must find something to give you in return."

They stared speechlessly as he probed amongst the things in the cart.

"I know there is something I have to do," he murmured absent-mindedly.

The two friends were still too speechless to remind him that he was supposed to be looking for a present for them. The Drawde carried on rummaging, then gave a squeal of delight and thrust a bundle of puppets into the hands of the Puppeteer.

"Oh, the darlings!" she exclaimed joyously, as she hugged her present. She held them out for Wizkid to see.

He looked at them and the Yesman, the Coalman, the Fireman, the Draughtsman and the Lighterman all looked back with their bright button eyes. They were fully restored with not a stitch out of place.

While they were examining the puppets the Drawde slipped quietly away and they only realised he had gone when he called, "Goodbye! Take care of the puppets, and share out those gorgeous grenades fairly."

They watched him trundle away without losing a single souvenir. As he was about to crash through a hedge he paused and shouted, "I've just remembered...those gorgeous grenades...they're magically explosive!" His voice trailed away and in the haze of dimensional radiation, his image seemed to blur; to shimmer for a second; to re-focus into four interwoven clones, then disappear, 'through a hedge, backwards'.

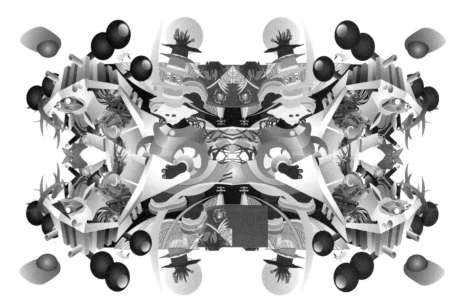

"Magic grenades! How lovely!" exclaimed the Puppeteer, clapping her hands gleefully.

"Yes, magic grenades! Magic grenades!" squawked a high pitched voice close by.

Wizkid and the Puppeteer looked around but they could not see the owner of the voice.

"As the celebrated 18th Century philosopher David Hume would have it, there is no way of proving conclusively that an effect can be attributed to a cause."

A rustling suggested that the chatter came from a spot in a hedge nearby.

"All that may be reasonably assumed is that cause and effect occur in association; the cause manifesting itself firstly and the effect secondly, thus we are at liberty to say that they are conjoined, but not that they are connected."

Neither Wizkid nor the Puppeteer had ever heard such drivel and they were curious to discover the source of the nonsense.

"Thus, when one talks about cause and effect, one has in mind the invariable observation of conjoined events."

They looked hard into the hedge and saw an enormous eye peering out at them.

"Now, magic has the distinction of not being definable in this way but may be described as a gratuitous manifestation of an effect or effects that is/are not conjoined to a cause or causes."

As if to add weight to its words, the speaker (if an eye can be called a speaker) emerged from its obscurity to station itself on top of the hedge. From this great height, it blinked down on the figures below.

"You may observe that my eye is in the process of being conjoined to a number of features which may or may not suggest to you a particular species under which they may be subsumed."

In spite of herself, the Puppeteer could not help blinking back at the creature, nor could she refrain from greeting the pompous whatever-it-was with a cheery, "Hello."

"Seeing that you are not such a bright student I shall manifest additional birdlike features to assist you in your deliberations."

Although the creature had ignored her greeting, the Puppeteer went on to tell it that she thought the additional bits and bobs were really quite helpful and added, "You are beginning to look like some kind of bird, except for the hands, of course."

The creature looked pleased and nodded the head 'bit or bob', graciously.

"Only you talk such gobbledygook that I think you must be a Gobbledygook."

The Gobbledygook looked cross and squawked ungraciously.

"Gobbledygook is a term that is used pejoratively by the intellectually retarded to disparage their intellectual superiors."

Oh! I do like riddles!" exclaimed the Puppeteer clapping her hands and giving Wizkid a big wink.

The Gobbledygook looked peeved and ignored her comment.

"Seeing that you are an even less bright student you might find it helpful to be told that what I said earlier means, amongst other things, that if you suck a magic grenade something unusual is sure to happen."

"Something unusually nice?"

The Gobbledygook looked both vexed and peeved and would say no more than, "Magic may be described as a gratuitous manifestation of an effect or effects."

"If only she wasn't so grumpy and could speak like everybody else, we could have a nice friendly chat."

"If only we had some cheese we could have some bread and cheese if only we had some bread," was all that the Gobbledygook would say.

Then she closed her eye and kept it firmly shut.

"Please don't go to sleep."

The Gobbledygook opened her eye and said, "I was not asleep. I was preventing all visual stimuli from reaching the brain and thereby aiding the clear functioning of the reflective process."

"Pardon?"

"I believe she means that she had her eye shut and was thinking," explained Wizkid.

"Do you always talk like that?" asked the Puppeteer as she peered enquiringly into the Gobbledygook's open eye.

"One's speech patterns are a function of acculturation modified by one's current emotional state plus numerous other matters that I do not have time to enter into atpresent."

The Puppeteer gazed at Wizkid in puzzlement.

"What she's saying is that she speaks that way more or less all the time... I think."

"I'm sorry she has so much difficulty talking properly, but that's no reason for her to shut her eye in that unfriendly way."

"Contrary to the Newtonian view that space exists absolutely, that is to say, independently of matter, the Leibnitzian view is that space, in a sense, is created by matter. Thus the space hereabouts, being created by my now fully manifest presence, does not require the presence of others," and she opened her eye and glowered at the figures below her.

"Why, the unfriendly...!" exclaimed the Puppeteer, who, in spite of the Gobbledygook's screwed up way of speaking, understood enough to know that she was being rude. "I've never heard such cheek in..." Her words trailed off as she struggled to reach the Gobbledygook.

"Help! Murder!" squawked the creature with her feathers fanning out in all directions. Next moment the bird lost her perch. Before they could stop her, she swooped down, grabbed the bag of gorgeous grenades and took to the sky.

No sooner was she in full flight than the bag slipped from her beak. Over and over it turned on its journey towards the earth, spilling its contents on the way. As the grenades fell through the air they exploded into a galaxy of falling stars.

Wizkid was all for chasing after the celestial display but the Puppeteer touched his arm and told him that first the puppets must be put somewhere safe.

"There dears, be good." The Puppeteer sat the Yesman and the four bearers astride a branch of a small tree. "Be good, especially to one another and everything will be all right."

She blew them a kiss and with Wizkid pulling her arm, they set off in quest of the stars.

59

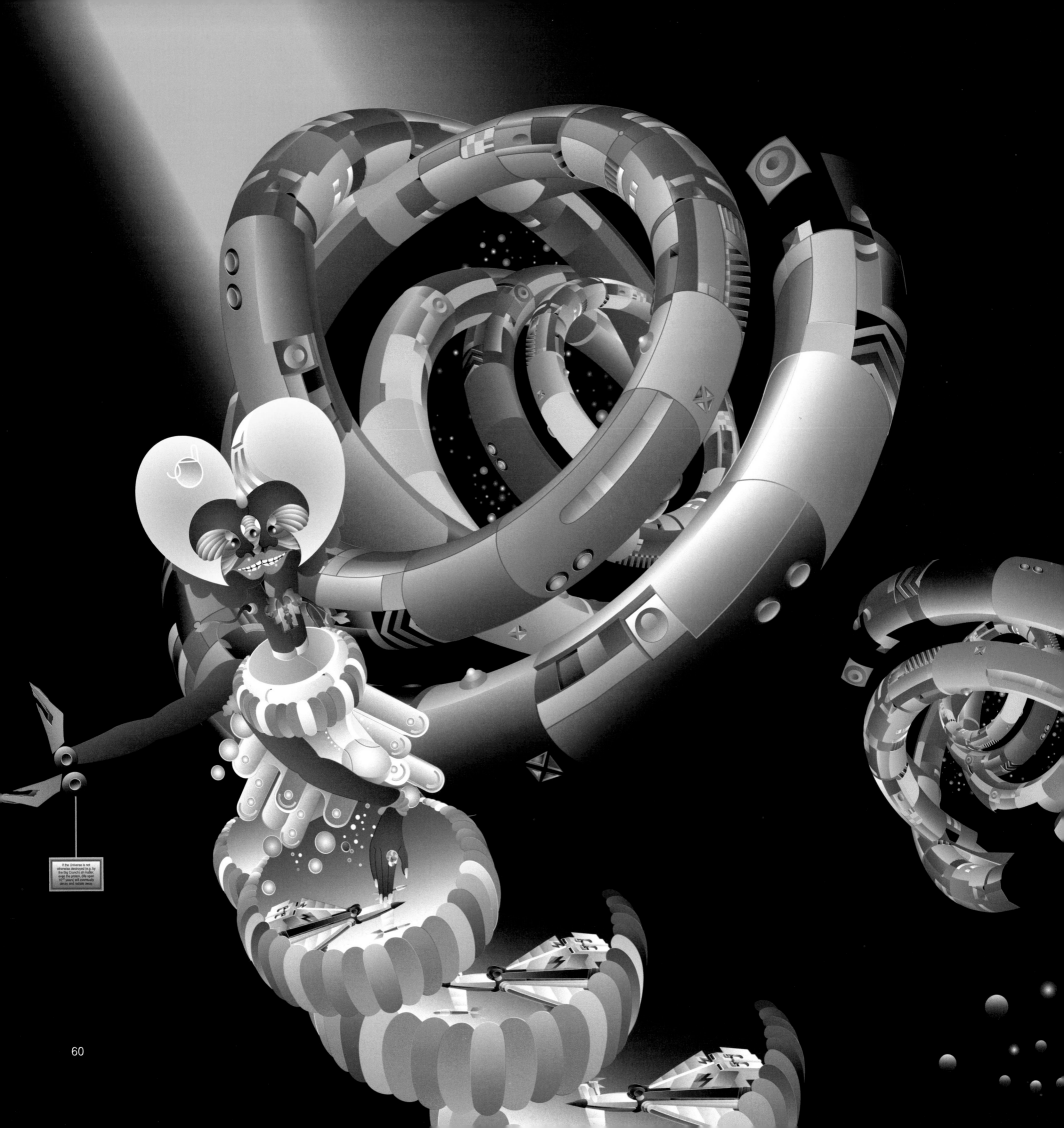

If the Universe is not otherwise destroyed (e.g. by the Big Crunch) all matter, even the protons, (life span 10^{31} years) will eventually decay and radiate away

KOOGY DEL BBOG

OK, yes, stars are really something, some of the most exciting things imaginable, but please, please spare a thought for her poor arm, nearly pulled from its socket.

"If you could just...

KALUZA KLEIN!"

The Puppeteer's sudden exclamation was not to be wondered at, for the two friends had re-entered the quadrangle into a galactic scene of breathtaking beauty. Before them lay a Milky Way of shimmering light. Faced by such splendour, the spirits of the two friends soared to fill the heavenly space. With her arms outstretched, the Puppeteer ran forward to embrace the galaxy; to compress its immensity to her, but, before she had time to mingle with its substance, it became insubstantial; became pure energy and radiated away

Her headlong rush brought her into near collision with a part of an altogether much more solid MK4 BOEING 337-2 Trans-Superspace Object (TSO) which was materialising out of the departing Galaxy. It levitated above them, beside them and around them, and left them gasping in wonder, as each morsel of technological succulence snapped into place to form the giant machine nicknamed by its fans, 'THE BOWELS OF SUPERSPACE'.

WARNING!

Always keep well clear of activated Trans-Superspace Objects. The superspacescapes they generate can have an annoying effect on people who get too close, e.g., if you are in Tuesday and are looking forward to enjoying a treat on Wednesday, you could find yourself in the following Friday sans treat. Even more annoying, you could find yourself on a different planet, orbiting a different star belonging to a different Galaxy, where there are no Wednesday treats.

INFO

THE BOWELS OF SUPERSPACE

Why the Bowels of Superspace? It probably has something to do with its designer, an Innuit Superspace engineer who had a health problem. He was having sleepless nights trying to come up with a way of assembling a modular Trans-Superspace Object that could be endlessly extended. His tension level was about to shoot through its escape velocity when he went down with a bout of tum trouble. Then he rumbled it. Assemble the modules after the fashion of intestines, that way they can curl up cosily with module being added to module ad infinitum, or for a quick job, the modules could be arranged concentrically.

"Isn't she beaut! Isn't **she beaut**!" enthused Wizkid when he had caught up with the Puppeteer. "It just has to be the greatest superspace cruncher ever... and that must be the transdimensional lock." He was pointing at a many faceted convex feature that hovered at the centre of the machine, "And what does that mean ?"

The object of Wizkid's interest was a nameplate inscribed:

KOOGY DEL BBOG, superspaceer.

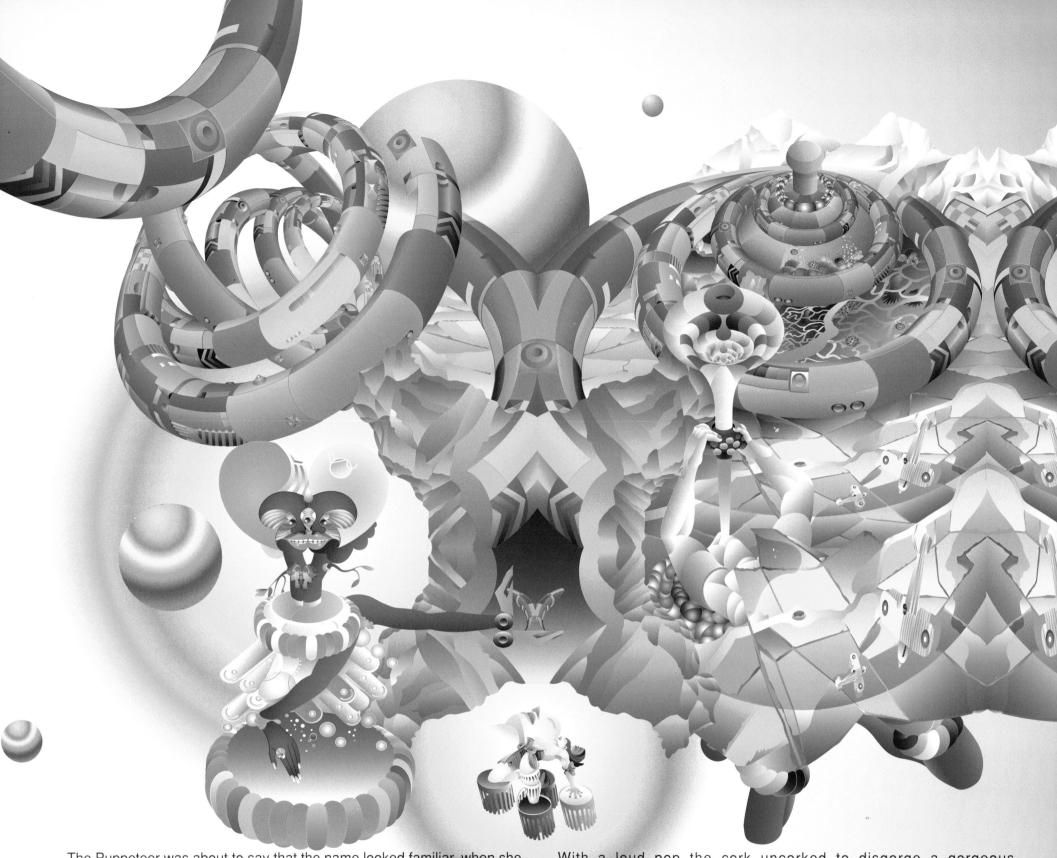

The Puppeteer was about to say that the name looked familiar, when she was interrupted by an eruption of the Cyclotronic Proton Smashers' latest top-of-the-charts intergalactic soundquake. The soundquake pulsated from the transdimensional lock as it underwent an extraordinary series of transformations. The two friends were fascinated, hypnotised, transfixed by its transdimensionality, until the soundquake stopped and stopped the lock in its tracks; stopped it from tracking through every shape in the Universe, and caused it to settle in the shape of a giant patent platinum plated Moët et Chandon champagne cork. Would you believe that?

With a loud pop the cork uncorked to disgorge a gorgeous nanosuperspacesuit.

"I'm Koogy," it declared.

"I'm very pleased to make your acquaintance..." said the Puppeteer, trying to sound as though it was a perfectly ordinary everyday event for her to be talking to what could well be the last word in centrifugal separators, "...and this is my friend who is looking for the Project Controller, Nilrem."

TRANSDIMENSIONALITY

"He ain't bogged down around these parts and that's for sure," replied Koogy as her nanosuperspacesuit unshelled from around her.

To smother a desire to shower the stranger with expressions of the boundless enthusiasm that he felt for 'THE BOWELS OF SUPERSPACE', Wizkid smiled and asked her what the 'DEL' part of her name stood for.

Koogy looked intently at the sign for a moment and said, "Er, well...it's German for...er...for 'of the'."

"I'm sure you're wrong about that. I'm sure it's French not German." said the Puppeteer winking at Wizkid.

"Is that a fact?"

"And what does 'BBOG' mean?" asked Wizkid, who preferred to keep the conversation easy, rather than explain that they were both wrong about the language to which the word 'DEL' belonged.

"You know, 'a bbog', as in, 'stuck in a bbog', giving us, 'Koogy of the Bbog'."

"But there's only one 'b' in 'bog'."

"Is that right?" said Koogy, scratching her head in consternation. "Well, in that case, the extra 'b' stands for 'book'."

"Why?"

"Because it refers to a 'Book Bog'."

"I've never heard of a 'Book Bog'."

"Ain't you never been bogged down in a book?" asked Koogy, directing the question at the Puppeteer, who had to confess that this did happen to her from time to time. "And weren't you bogged down a while back by the Gobbledygook?"

"How do you know about the Gobbledygook?" intervened Wizkid.

Koogy turned and said, "Didn't I tell you? It was the Drawde. He dropped me the word when he dropped off my name plate. Ha! Ha! Ho! Ho! Get it ...dropped off my nameplate. No? Well, like I was saying...what was I saying?"

"But how did the Drawde know about our meeting with the Gobbledygook?"

"I'd have thought a couple of clued-up guys like you would've spotted the answer to that one by now. It's very simple...the Drawde is the Author incognito, you know, in disguise. Some dumb Author he is too...tried to base my character on the Mad March Hare. I soon put him right on that one. He didn't get a wink of sleep all last night worrying about it...he'll be mighty glad to have me back on the other side of superspace and that's for sure."

They listened to Koogy quite unable to believe their ears.

"Mind though, you've gotta humour him, after all, should he have a mind to go off to fetch a cup of coffee,° he could lose track of the story. Whatever you do, don't kick up a fuss, that makes him nervous...who knows what could happen then...Holy Moses!...He could even spill the coffee on his computer and that'd finish off the whole caboose, you, me and everything hereabouts."

"I don't believe one word you say," said the Puppeteer defiantly, "I'm not in a story, I'm a flesh and blood person."

"He's some crazy Author making you talk that way," said Koogy.

"How dare you!" exclaimed the Puppeteer in great anger. "What I say is what I say, and nobody makes me say anything I don't want to."

In her distress she turned to Wizkid for comfort and support.

"We are not in a book, are we?" she asked tearfully.

Wizkid thought he saw a shadow of a smile flit through the Puppeteer's tears. Nevertheless he put an arm round her shoulder and whispered in her ear, "Look, cool it. Quality control can be a bit glitchy...some of these robots turn out a bit loony...so we'll have to humour her. OK?"

"He's a great mate of mine...the Author," Wizkid said aloud, "Only last night we were chatting about the very chapter that we're in now and it was agreed that my next line should be ... 'It's been great meeting you, but we must hit the road.'"

"Well, that ain't the version I got," objected Koogy.

"No?"

"No, I reckon you'll have to stay awhiles."

"If it's all the same to you, we'll vamoose."

"Suit yourselves, but you won't get far!"

"We'll see about that," said Wizkid, defiantly.

He took his companion by the arm and led her away, back into the Maze. After turning several corners they were distressed to find themselves exactly where they had started.

"Hello again," said Koogy cheerily.

Wizkid was all set to give vent to a rising feeling of anger, when Koogy forestalled him.

"Now don't get sore...relax! Remember, we're all in the same book." She paused to give them time to gather themselves. "Look at it this way, we've just gotta follow along, whereas the Author...the poor sucker...has gotta work hard on the story, not to mention those crazy graphics." As she spoke she touched their arms in the friendliest of gestures.

"You're on the bull's eye about one thing though...we're not actually in the book right now, we're still on the computer. At least I think we're still on the computer, or maybe we've gotten into the book already. No...the computer...no...no...the book. That guy really has me confused, I'm not sure where the heck we are!"

Neither Wizkid nor the Puppeteer believed for one moment that they were characters in a book, nor were they going to accept the ridiculous notion that they were knocking around inside some computer or other. However, Koogy was so well meaning that they could not be angry with her any longer.

"Although..." thought Wizkid, "...she is as mad as a March Hare".

To change the subject, Wizkid asked about the Gobbledygook.

"Poor gal," said Koogy sighing, "at one time she was bogged down in a bbog for a whole year."

"What on earth did she live on in all that time?" asked the Puppeteer with concern.

"She ate books and drank bbog water."

"Surely that must have made her very sick?" The Puppeteer was beginning to feel sorry for the Gobbledygook, in spite of her unpleasant encounter with the creature.

"Real sick", confirmed Koogy sadly, "it gave her verbal diarrhoea."

"Poor thing! What kind of books did she eat?"

"Mostly very hard ones such as works on astronomy, which made her head spin like a top, and on chemistry which..."

" ...which upset her poor tummy," interrupted the Puppeteer.

"Right," agreed Koogy.

"She must have found it very difficult to settle down at night," sympathised the Puppeteer, having suffered from the problem herself when she'd had a bout of 'flu.

"For a spell she did," admitted Koogy. "until she started to eat books with titles such as THE HOUSEHOLD ACCOUNTS OF THE HOUSE OF YORK, 1492 - 1504, which sent her to sleep pronto."

"What a boring diet. Why didn't she eat adventure or mystery books? I'm sure she'd have found those really yummy."

"For two reasons," answered Koogy.

"1.   As a rule, people don't get bogged down in books of that sort.

2.   Even if there were any around she'd be too proud to be found eating them."

SPICE

"That's silly," said the Puppeteer. "Anyway, I hope I never get caught in a bbog."

"The Author is doing his darndest to avoid it."

The two friends chose to ignore Koogy's last remark and to keep the conversation away from that disagreeable subject, Wizkid asked her if the Gobbledygook had taken anything for her illness.

"Three spoonfuls of Doctor Getwell's book, 1000 BEST CURES, dissolved in bbog water," came the reply.

"What happened?" asked the Puppeteer, anxiously.

Koogy shook her head sadly and answered, "She nearly choked to death on some lumps that had not quite dissolved. They had come from the chapter on gall stones, would you believe!"

"What did she eat after that?"

"Nothing for a while. Well, not exactly nothing. She did eat a book called THE TEN DIMENSIONAL MAZE, a light fluffy morsel that was worse than useless. She would have died but for the fact that some of the Bbogsiders took her some titbits from the book, EXOTIC DISHES FROM THE SPICE PLANETS. At first she would not touch them, but eventually she was persuaded that they would give her no trouble. In fact, they did her a power of good and as her strength returned, so did her confidence. Shortly afterwards she managed to get herself unbbogged. She's OK now, but her lingo has been screwed up ever since, poor gal."

The Puppeteer was delighted with the story and clapped her hands gleefully, whilst Wizkid tried to think of something to say that would keep the conversation from returning to the worrying subject of books and computers.

"Now that you have all but blown the gaff we must be on our way to meet the PM."

Wizkid could not believe his ears. The words formed in his mouth expressed neither his thoughts nor his feelings. They were not his words nor did he know anyone with the initials PM.

His bewilderment was not lost on Koogy, who told him not to worry. "It's that dumb Author again. He's making you say things that aren't in character, just to keep the story going." She gave an exclamation of exasperation and concluded with, "Well, I suppose I'd better do the obvious...no originality that guy...and tell you where the PM hangs out."

Wizkid thought, "That crazy Koogy! She really is a nutter!"

The Puppeteer thought, "The poor dear! What can be the matter with her?"

Koogy thought, "Those dumb kids! They're being taken for a ride!"

PLANETS

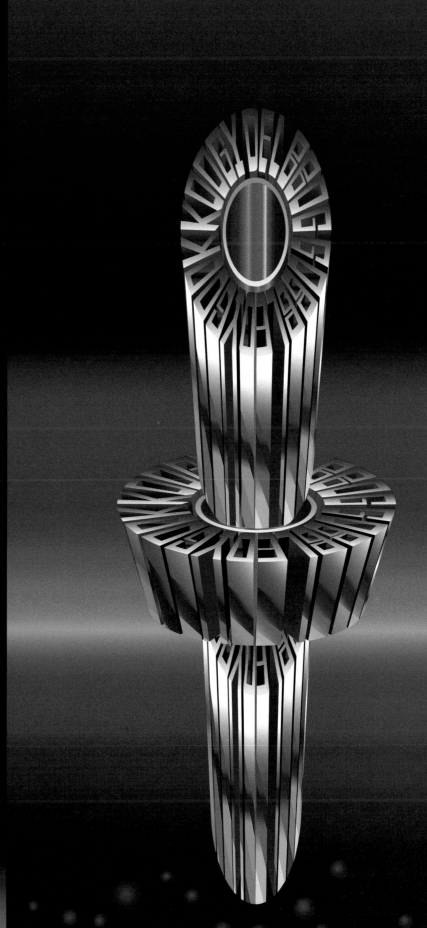

THE VENDING MACHINE

INFO

Although the Ten Dimensional Maze is a marvellous invention it still has a few problems. Apart from the trouble with hackers, its design is so advanced that the programmers of the programmers are running behind. Until they cross the finishing line, the Ten Dimensional Maze is going to flip now and again, causing the darnedest things to happen.

Some experts say that it is not so much a programming problem, but more to do with the hardware. There are so many layers (27), that in some areas the Ten Dimensional Maze may be functioning non-linearly and as a result is inclined to behave outlandishly.

Somewhere in the Ten Dimensional Maze, far from the spot where the two friends were looking dumbfoundedly at an empty space, a vending machine suddenly materialised; a perfectly ordinary vending machine. Or so it seemed. Actually, it was rather like one of those contraptions to be found on the LMS Railway or the Ghan in the first half of the 20th Century. This particular machine was called Chocolate and was home to that cosmic gateway to paradise, the Andromeda **Ripple Crunchy Chocy Bar with Scrumptiously Toasted Mouth-Watering Tropicana Betelnuts**. How the machine got there nobody knows, although its presence was no surprise, because one of the more endearing characteristics of the Ten Dimensional Maze is a tendency to attract bits of the better class of flotsam and jetsam from just about anywhere at any time.

LOVELY!

Not so lovely is the annoying way in which the goodies once entrapped there become deucedly difficult to locate. Many people have struggled unsuccessfully to find them, while others with no particular interest in the goodies, have stumbled upon them within a few minutes of entering the Maze.

IF YOU WANT IT YOU WON'T FIND IT AND IF YOU DON'T WANT IT YOU WILL

Which is why, shortly after leaving Koogy, our two friends, with ne'er a thought in their heads about Andromeda **Ripple Crunchy Chocy Bar with Scrumptiously Toasted Mouth-Watering Tropicana Betelnuts**, happened upon the vending machine.

Wizkid:	Which planet has it come from?
The Puppeteer:	Where's the speechport?
Wizkid:	How many megabytes does it have?
The Puppeteer:	Is that slot the speechport?
Wizkid:	I've heard of Apple Computers but not the chocolate variety.
The Puppeteer:	Perhaps it has a thoughtport?

To bite into an Andromeda **Ripple Crunchy Chocy Bar with Scrumptiously Toasted Mouth-Watering Tropicana Betelnuts** is to enjoy the most satisfying pleasure in the Galaxy. There is a problem though...the moment the desire to indulge grabs you, the vending machine flips to another part of the Ten Dimensional Maze.

Not having a sweet tooth, the Proprietors have never experienced this manoeuvre. They are deeply mystified by the poor sales performance of their prize product, especially as in a bid to tempt punters to part with their money, they have spent billions of ecu on subliminal and submarine advertising.

SUBMARINE ADVERTISING

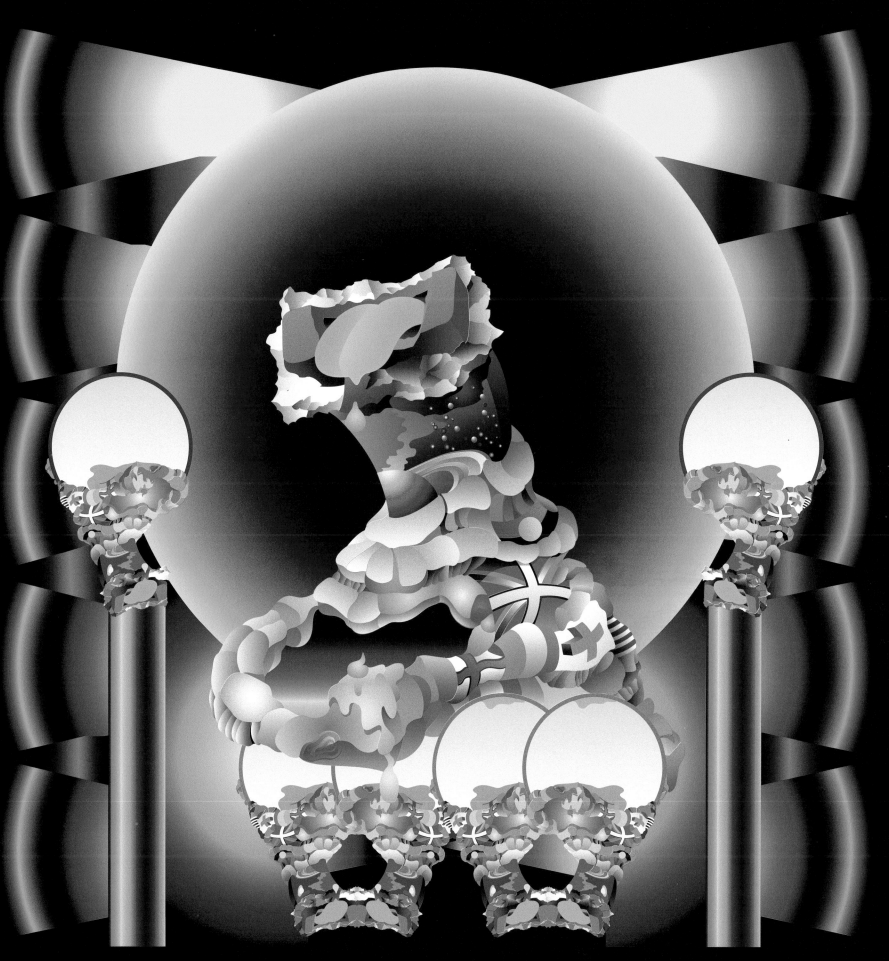

SUBLIMINAL

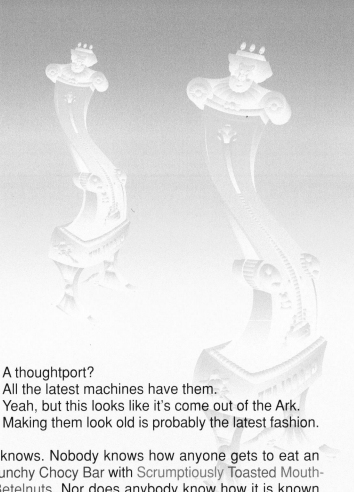

Wizkid:	A thoughtport?
The Puppeteer:	All the latest machines have them.
Wizkid:	Yeah, but this looks like it's come out of the Ark.
The Puppeteer:	Making them look old is probably the latest fashion.

The truth is...nobody knows. Nobody knows how anyone gets to eat an Andromeda Ripple Crunchy Chocy Bar with Scrumptiously Toasted Mouth-Watering Tropicana Betelnuts. Nor does anybody know how it is known that the Andromeda Ripple Crunchy Chocy Bar with Scrumptiously Toasted Mouth-Watering Tropicana Betelnuts is the most satisfying pleasure in the Galaxy.

ADVERTISING?

Wizkid:	An Andromeda Ripple Crunchy Chocy Bar with Scrumptiously Toasted Mouth-Watering Tropicana Betelnuts is the most satisfying pleasure in the Galaxy.
The Puppeteer:	I beg your pardon.
Wizkid:	An Androm...Why am I saying this?
The Puppeteer:	You OK?
Wizkid:	I have a sudden yearning for an Andromeda Rip ...

Somewhere in the Ten Dimensional Maze, far from the spot where the two friends were looking dumbfoundedly at an empty space, a vending machine suddenly materialised; a perfectly ordinary vending machine. Or so it seemed. Actually it was rather like one of those contraptions to be found on the LMS Railway or the Ghan...

IF YOU WANT IT YOU WON'T FIND IT AND IF YOU DON'T WANT IT YOU WILL

Wizkid just had to find an Andromeda Ripple Crunchy Chocy Bar with Scrumptiously Toasted Mouth-Watering Tropicana Betelnuts even if it meant searching the Maze from top to bottom. The poor Puppeteer did not share his passion. Even so she was dragged in Wizkid's wake, not screaming, not even complaining, but just wishing that her companion was not in such a hurry. If only they could spend a little time exploring all the lovely nooks and crannies that beckoned enticingly at each turn in the Maze.

INFO

A word of caution. Should you ever find yourself in the Ten Dimensional Maze, do not be deceived by the lush exteriors of those lovely nooks and crannies, for sometimes behind them lurk fearsome Ten Dimensional Dilemmas. Avoid rushing headlong into them, for they should be tackled only after many years of travelling up to London on the 8.30, doing the Times's crossword puzzle. Or failing that, the possession of a clutch of first class honours degrees in the better subjects from the better universities might just about serve instead.

INFO

When not being worn, Koogy's brooch is set in a plaque that contains a really luscious deception. If you are a 20th or 21st Century reader and would like to have a crack at unmasking the tomfoolery, well, you can do so next time you are in Japan. The plaque and brooch are to be seen in the Kyoto Museum of Modern Art, so pop along there and if you have difficulty finding the brooch, ask for 'Calvary 1'. But you must hurry for it will be there only until the middle of the 21st Century.

So, having worked the Puppeteer to a frazzle, did Wizkid find that wondrous confection?

Well, not exactly. His appetite wasn't so much satisfied, no, it just ceased to exist. And it had something to do with Koogy. The craving left him the moment he set eyes on an updated Mark 2 Koogy smelling of fresh paint and gleaming from a recent session in the spray booth. (Later he reckoned that it was the smell of the paint that had clobbered his craving for the Proprietors' Prize Product.)

She was installed in one of those lovely nooks and crannies, radiant in her new-found glory, sitting at a heavily carved invisible desk and peering, first into the screen of a Barco Calibrator monitor (circa 1995), then at a book which lay open on the table. Koogy was so absorbed in what she was doing that she did not notice the approach of the two friends, until the Puppeteer gave a discreet cough, prompting the Superspaceer to turn from her task and give them a warm greeting.

They returned her welcome with a little less enthusiasm, for they had mixed feelings about seeing Koogy again. To cover the shortness of his response, Wizkid asked her what she was doing.

"I'm trying to figure out where the heck we are...on the computer or in the book." (A dilemma, yes, but not as tricky as those that are to be found in the really luscious lovely nooks and crannies where a tangle of anomalies, deceptions, divergences and uncertainties can drag even the most sober minded boffin into an infinity of nothing.)

Wizkid was not pleased with the reply to his question, whereas his companion, either because she had missed the point of Koogy's answer or because she chose to ignore it, declared, if it were a story book that Koogy had there on the desk, nothing would give her greater pleasure than to have it read to her, "If you don't mind, that is," she concluded.

"Be my guest."

"Is it a true story?" asked Wizkid.

"As true as you're standing there, see for yourself," replied Koogy, beckoning them to come closer. They bent over the book and she started to read aloud.

KOOGY'S DESK
Koogy's desk is made of virtual matter, a first cousin of shadow matter. Shadow Matter is invisible and is detectable only because it responds to the gravitational pull of ordinary matter. Virtual Matter differs from only in its being detectable by touch.
Virtual matter is found only in the Ten Dimensional Maze.

A VERY PROMISING PM

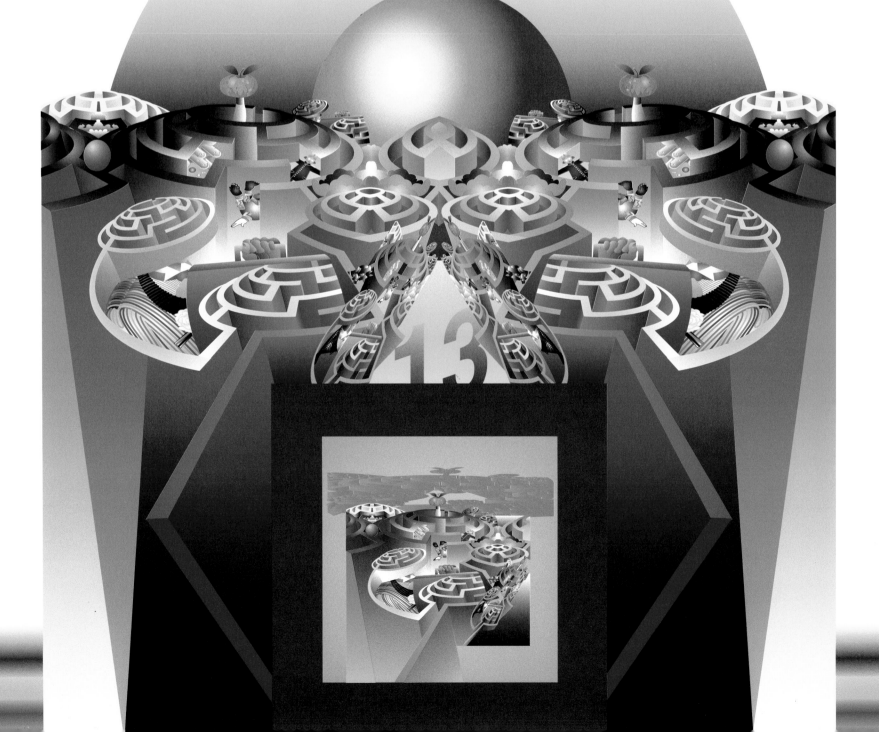

The man looked searchingly at the two friends. After a moment or so he said vaguely, "You must be the young folks Koogy told me about."

"Koogy?" queried Wizkid.

"Yes, you know, our superspace-trotting friend...the hi-tech young lady who sent you along to see me."

The two friends stared mutely at their new acquaintance, whilst the latter introduced himself.

"I'm the PM; the Prime Minister, that's me."

"Good day, Your Honour," said the Puppeteer, stressing the 'Your Honour' out of respect for the PM's position. "Only it's not such a good day really," she added, glancing up at the sky.

AT THIS POINT IN HER READING, KOOGY WAS INTERRUPTED BY THE PUPPETEER LETTING LOOSE A GLEEFUL, "THE STORY'S ABOUT US, HOW MARVELLOUS!"

"Not such a good day," said the PM, following the Puppeteer's upward glance. "I'm glad you mentioned that, otherwise it would most certainly have gone unnoticed; not have been noticed at all."

He put his hand into a carpet bag he was carrying and pulled out a stylus and a Newton Message Pad. "Not such a good day," he repeated aloud as he wrote it down. "That's to remind me to do something about it."

"I beg your pardon, Your Honour," said the Puppeteer, "but it isn't possible to do anything about the weather."

"Of course, I don't really mean to *do* anything, you understand...no not really."

"Then why have you made a note to do something?" asked Wizkid.

"Ha! I'm very glad you asked me, yes very, very glad. I made a note to remind me to **promise** to do something about it," he replied, "which is, as I'm sure you will agree, quite different from actually **doing** something about it; no, not at all the same as **doing** something."

"How could you be so dishonest!"

"It's not easy and requires training of course, but a few people do have a natural bent for it. For example, I have no difficulty in promising anything you care to name; absolutely anything."

Then he paused to ponder before going on in a voice full of pride, "Even at an early age my teachers would write in my school reports such comments as, 'A very promising pupil', 'He shows great promise', 'We have never had a more promising boy'; things like that, you understand. The school promises were very large and our motto was:

'I Promise to Pay the Bearer on Demand the Sum of Five Hundred Ecu .'

So, you see, with a background like that I could hardly fail to live up to my early promise; no, could not fail at all."

"I do see," said the Puppeteer, pensively. "Are you certain you have the motto right? I'm sure I've seen it, or something very like it, printed on bank notes."

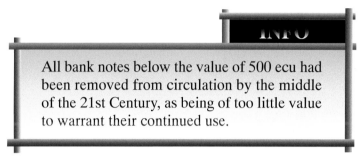

All bank notes below the value of 500 ecu had been removed from circulation by the middle of the 21st Century, as being of too little value to warrant their continued use.

"You don't surprise me... it's a very good motto, you know, yes, a very, very good motto."

Then he fell silent and looked dreamily into the middle distance.

"He is probably reliving his school days," thought the Puppeteer. "What a curious school it must have been. I wonder..."

"As you know so much about such matters, perhaps you have come across our other motto somewhere or other. It goes like this:

'I Promise to Tell the Truth, the Whole Truth and Nothing but the Truth, so Help Me God.'

AGAIN THE PUPPETEER INTERRUPTED KOOGY TO SAY, "IT SOUNDS RATHER LIKE SOMETHING PEOPLE SAY IN COURT."

"It sounds rather like something people say in court," said the Puppeteer.

"Very likely! Very likely! A good motto like that is bound to be used in all sorts of places."

Then the PM paused and looked enquiringly at the Puppeteer, "In a court, you say. Would that be a tennis court, by chance?"

"No, not a tennis court, Your Honour."

"Oh, what a pity! I'm sure a motto like that would be most useful in a tennis court, most useful indeed...most use..."

"Excuse me," said the Puppeteer hurriedly, to stop him bumbling on, "do you happen to know where we may find Nilrem, the Project Controller?"

Instead of answering the question, the PM just stared at her in puzzlement. After a while, he asked her if she would mind repeating what she had just said. She did so, slowly, clearly and deliberately. The PM listened to her attentively and when she had finished he said, "That's not a very useful motto, you know; not useful at all."

"But, Your Honour, it isn't meant to be a motto."

"I'm so glad to hear that; so very glad. It would have let you down sooner or later; sooner or later let you down." He paused and then added, "Of course, if it isn't a motto it must be something else, you know...that's only logical."

"Well, yes, Your Honour, it's a question."

"Ha! That's very interesting; very interesting indeed. It makes all the difference, you understand, because questions require answers but mottoes require...but mottoes...it's called grammar or etiquette or something like that," said the PM, looking blankly from one to the other of his two listeners.

"Now that I know it's a question, it makes excellent sense; it's as plain as plain; as plain as..."

The two friends thought they had never seen anyone look so bewildered as the PM, when he said, 'as plain, as plain'.

"Would you mind very much," he went on, looking appealingly at the Puppeteer, "repeating your question just one more time?"

She did as she was asked.

"I'm very glad you put that question, otherwise it would most likely have gone unasked," said the PM, as he wrote it down on his Newton Message Pad.

"That's to remind me to promise to find the NPC," he explained, putting away his NMP and then he went on sadly, "Of course, I never shall find him; never find him at all."

"Don't people get annoyed when you fail to keep your promises?" remonstrated Wizkid.

"Either they get annoyed or else...or else..."

"Or else what?"

"They get very, very annoyed, you know," he concluded.

"Doesn't that make things rather difficult for you?" asked the Puppeteer sympathetically.

"Either it makes things rather difficult or else...or else..."

"Or else what?" she encouraged.

"It makes things rather awkward," explained the PM unhappily.

He looked from one to the other of the friends as though to make sure they were still there and said, "Until, that is, I promise them a great many new things, particularly new ideas, they love new ideas. Then they stop being annoyed and things stop being difficult or awkward. That's why I'm always looking out for new things to promise."

"I don't see that bamboozling people solves anything in the end," objected Wizkid.

"Not in the end, no, but then if you can keep things at the beginning there will be no end...that's only logical."

"How do you manage that?"

The PM looked crestfallen and replied, "I don't, as a rule, I'm afraid. As hard as I try, the beginning always gets away in the end; always gets away."

Then he cheered up a little and said, "But I have a new idea for tackling the problem."

"How interesting," remarked the Puppeteer brightly. "What do you plan to do?"

"Nothing, I don't plan to do anything at all," said the PM, irritably. "What I said was that I have a new idea."

"What is your new idea then?" asked the Puppeteer soothingly.

"To form a plan. My new idea is to form a plan."

"When do you think you will form your plan?"

"Never, I shall never actually form a plan; no, not actually form a plan. I have only a new idea to form a plan, which is not at all the same thing, you know."

The Puppeteer was puzzled by the PM's statement. A moment or two passed as she pondered over it and she was just beginning to feel that, with only a little more effort, she might be able to sort it out, when the PM spoke again.

"Well, I must be on my way," he declared. "I promised not to attend a Cabinet beating, so I must be sure not to miss it at all costs. You may walk along with me if you wish or, for that matter, you can..."

"For that matter, we can what?" asked Wizkid, for the PM had paused.

"For that matter you can come along with me if you don't want to, either way it's the same to me."

They had not walked very far when the PM asked Wizkid if he knew how to read maps.

"Sort of."

"Excellent," exclaimed the PM. Then he turned to the Puppeteer and asked her, in a casual way, if she just happened to have a map of the World in her pocket, "To find out where we are," he explained.

The reason the PM gave for wanting a map is not strictly true. For many years he had been trying to get to the Big Apple, but all that he had managed to do was wear down both the soles of his shoes and the path through the Ten Dimensional Maze.

After the first two hundred years of wandering, a brilliant idea struck him. Why not buttonhole stray travellers and wheedle a map out of them? This ploy had kept him busy without success for the last hundred years and will continue to do so for almost as long as the Maze continues to exist, at the end of which period an even more brilliant idea will strike him. Why not ask someone who knows the way, how to get to the Big Apple?

IF YOU WANT IT YOU WON'T FIND IT AND IF YOU DON'T WANT IT YOU WILL

"But, Your Honour, you won't find this Maze on a map of the World. What you need is a ten dimensional plan of the Maze."

The PM looked at her queerly and said in a perplexed voice, "I had always supposed the Maze to be somewhere or other on the World, you know."

"What I mean, is that it's too small to appear on a map of the World."

"Yours is not a well-mannered sort of map; not well-mannered at all. I really don't think I want to be acquainted with it, so I should be obliged if you would leave it in your pocket."

"Not well-mannered, Your Honour?"

The PM seemed not to hear her, but looked thoughtfully into space. Then, as though he had made up his mind about something or other, he murmured, "After all, if the Maze is gracious enough to allow the map to occupy a place in it, then the least the map can do is to return the compliment; that's only good manners."

The party walked on a few more paces until the PM murmured in a far away voice, "Where I come from the maps have everything on them; absolutely everything; all the streets and all the houses in the streets and all the rooms inside the houses and all the things inside the rooms, like corkscrews and tea-bells and computers and books and reject art and all the chapter headings inside the books and even the page numbers, you know."

"Why, your maps must be as big ... as big as the World!" exclaimed the Puppeteer in amazement.

"Bigger, much bigger,"

"And very awkward to carry about, I should think?"

"Nobody ever carries them about. In fact, nobody ever unfolds them either," explained the PM sadly, "because there isn't a space large enough, being bigger than the World as they are, you understand."

"They can't be much use then?"

"Not much use perhaps, but they are very well-mannered."

"If I had a choice," said the Puppeteer thoughtfully, "I'd prefer to have a useful map, rather than a well-mannered one...I think."

"If you had a choice you could choose to live in one of our maps; if you had a choice, that is."

"I don't see how, if they are only printed on paper!"

"Where you come from, maybe, but our maps are not like that; not like that at all. You can walk about in them just like we are doing in this Maze," explained the PM, and then he added after a moment's reflection, "not just like we are doing exactly; like we are doing only more perfectly, if you know what I mean. Yes, that's how it is...everything is perfect in our maps. The countryside is beautiful with clear running rivers full of fish, the cities orderly, the houses clean and airy, the beds soft, the food well cooked and plentiful. All the TSVs, trains, trams and buses run on time and... and the sun shines through a peerless POLLUTION FREE sky."

"How lovely!" exclaimed the Puppeteer wide eyed, "I'd just adore living there!"

"You could too," said the PM eagerly, "only..."

"Only you can't unfold your maps," concluded the Puppeteer sadly.

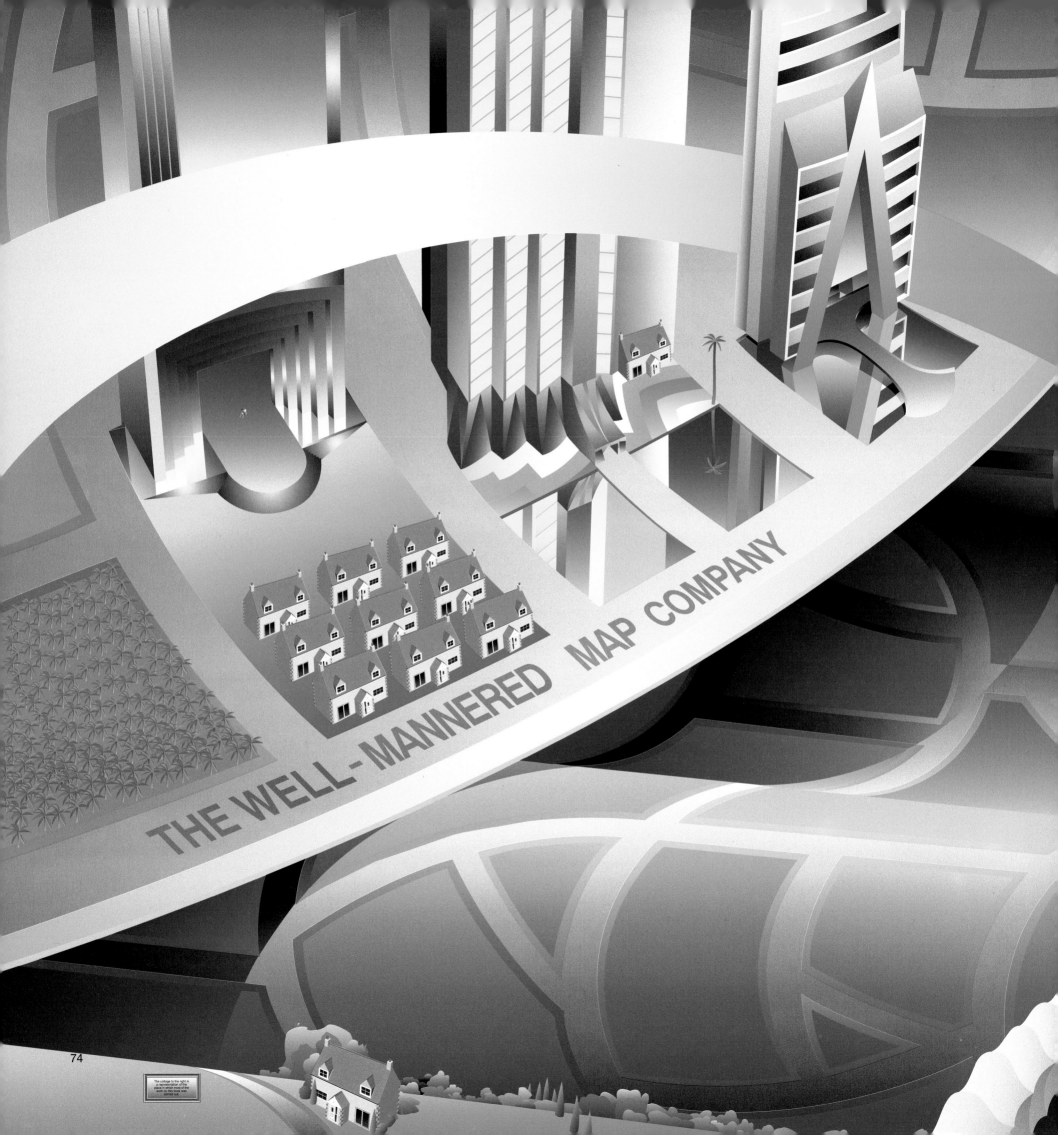

THE WELL - MANNERED MAP COMPANY

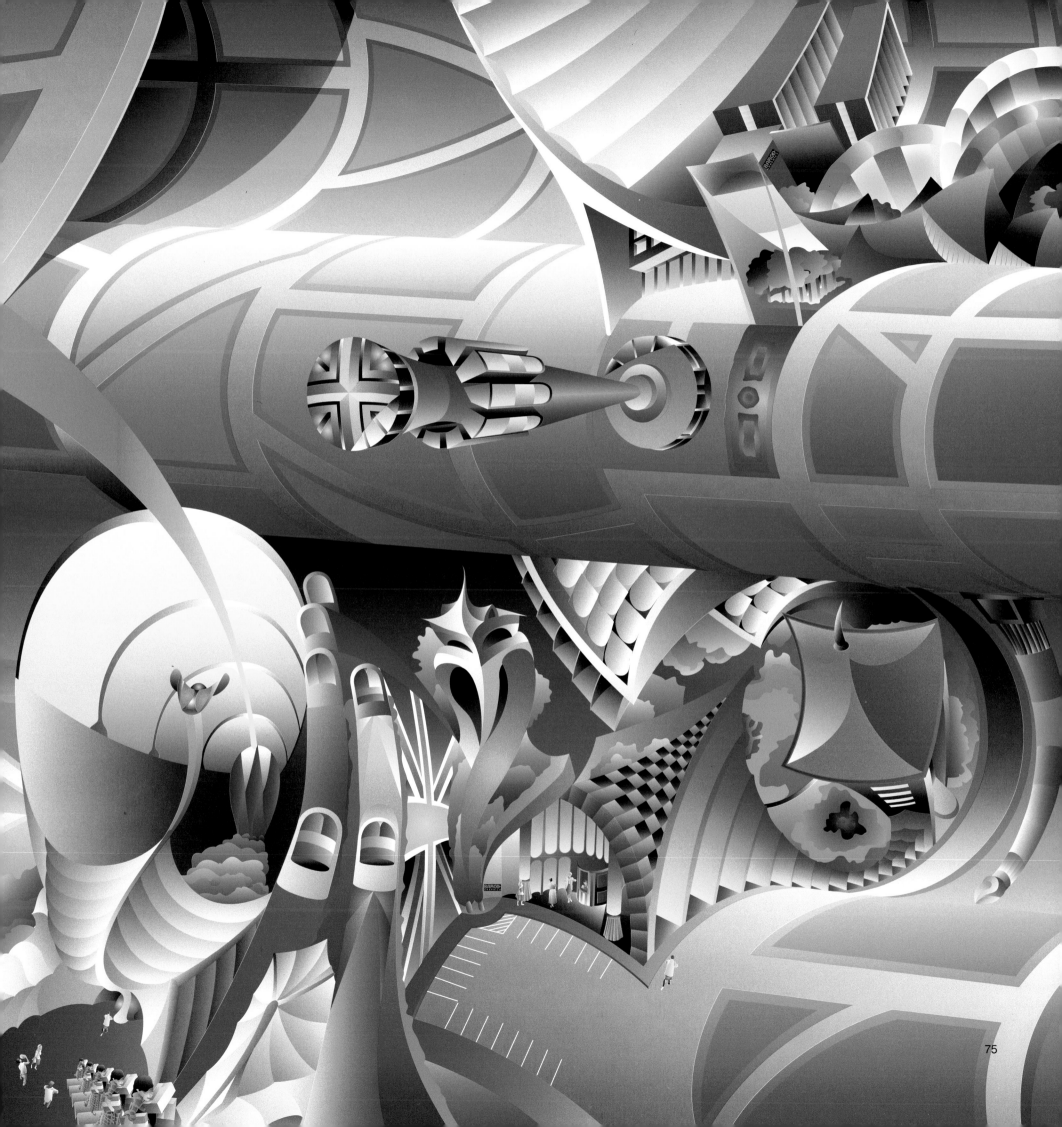

"Who told you that?" he demanded in a voice that was remarkably fierce for such a mild person. "That's a State Secret; a secret of state, that is."

"Why, you did of course, Your Honour."

"I did?" queried the PM, looking about him in a frightened sort of way. "How was I dressed at the time, do you happen to remember?"

"Well, as it was only a few moments ago, I would have to be a very stupid person to have forgotten so soon."

"Was I wearing pin-striped trousers and jacket, a miseryjoy hat and carrying a carpet bag?"

"Of course you were, only..."

"And what am I wearing at the moment?"

"The same, except that you are not wearing a miseryjoy hat. You were and still are wearing an amazing hat."

"Then it *was* me," stammered the PM. "Or someone who was disguised to look just like me? A spy, perhaps?"

The word 'spy' so alarmed him that he missed his step and would surely have fallen into a lower dimension had the two friends not been there to support him.

INFO

Sometimes the Ten Dimensional Maze behaves rather like a car seat belt in reverse. Sudden movement can release the unwary from the default dimensions and propel him/her/it into other dimensions. That is to say, it can behave in a perfectly ordered, disorderly way, when it's not behaving in an imperfectly disordered, orderly way.

EXAMPLE

In a week from now the Maze will depart from its perfectly ordered, disorderly routine and do an imperfectly disordered, orderly flip through superspace to a location that looks remarkably like Hanging Rock on St. Valentine's Day 1900.

A school picnic party will be in progress. Four young ladies will leave the main group. Two of the four, with their maths mistress, will feel the dimensional radiation of the Maze, succumb to its attraction and enter a parallel universe that is identical to the one they leave, except of course for their absence from it.

Those of you who would like to know more about this future event can do so by reading the past account of it in Joan Lindsay's enchanting book, PICNIC AT HANGING ROCK and its sequel, or by getting a copy of the film from your local video shop. Best of all, if you are a 22nd Century reader, get the SR (Superreality) nodule and mingle with the characters, smell the eucalypts on a summer's day, but be careful not to disappear with the young ladies.

Oh yes, if you are a 20th Century or early 21st Century reader, you may be wondering how the Maze is able to do the impossible and flip backwards in time. No problem...Superreality!

REMEMBER

SUPERREALITY = VIRTUAL REALITY + VIRTUAL INFINITE MEMORY

SR+10DM = IT"LL BLOW YOUR MIND FROM HERE TO ETERNITY

PARALLEL UNIVERSE

Once the PM had regained his balance, an earnest expression filled his face.

"Was this person wearing a striped shirt and white tie and a miseryjoy hat in his buttonhole, do you remember?"

"Of course," confirmed the Puppeteer, impatiently.

"That proves it," declared the PM, triumphantly. "He was a spy, because only a spy could be so well informed about the way I dress."

This line of reasoning satisfied him for a while, then some doubt must have crept back into his mind, for he asked Wizkid if he had seen the spy.

"No," Wizkid replied firmly, "it was you who told us about the map."

"In that case," said the PM sorrowfully, "in that case it's me, I'm the spy." He stopped in his tracks as tears welled up in his eyes.

"I did so want to continue being the PM. I want to be the PM so much." He went on to declare between sobs that he would promise everything to everyone, if only he could continue to be the PM.

Until now the Puppeteer had been steadily losing patience with the PM, but seeing him standing there crying so pitifully, softened her heart. She took hold of his hand and stroked it gently, whilst in a soothing voice she said, "Of course you can continue to be the PM, because you are the PM. Why, if you were a spy you would be sort of...sort of quick-witted and lively you know, not at all like you are."

"Do you really think so?" he asked, brightening up.

"Of course we do," she replied, looking at Wizkid for support, who in response smiled weakly at the PM.

In response to his response, the Puppeteer gave Wizkid a big wink.

"You know I never really thought I was a spy; not a real spy," he said making his way along the path again. "Only..."

Once more he looked as though he might burst into tears, but he rallied bravely and continued, "...only, people call me so many names that I often think that I might be someone else."

Then he lowered his voice and mumbled something that the two friends could not hear.

"What was that you said?" asked Wizkid.

The PM raised his voice to explain, "I was just repeating my school mottoes to myself...to give me courage; just to give me courage that's all." Then he lowered his voice again and continued mumbling until once more his voice rose and he said, "They are very good mottoes and get used in all sorts of places. Yes, in all sorts of places, on bank...on the banks of

not clear about, they are not used an awful lot on tennis cour awful..."

The last part of the sentence was drowned by a loud noise that c the direction in which they were walking.

"Ha!" exclaimed the PM, increasing his pace, "the Cabinet be

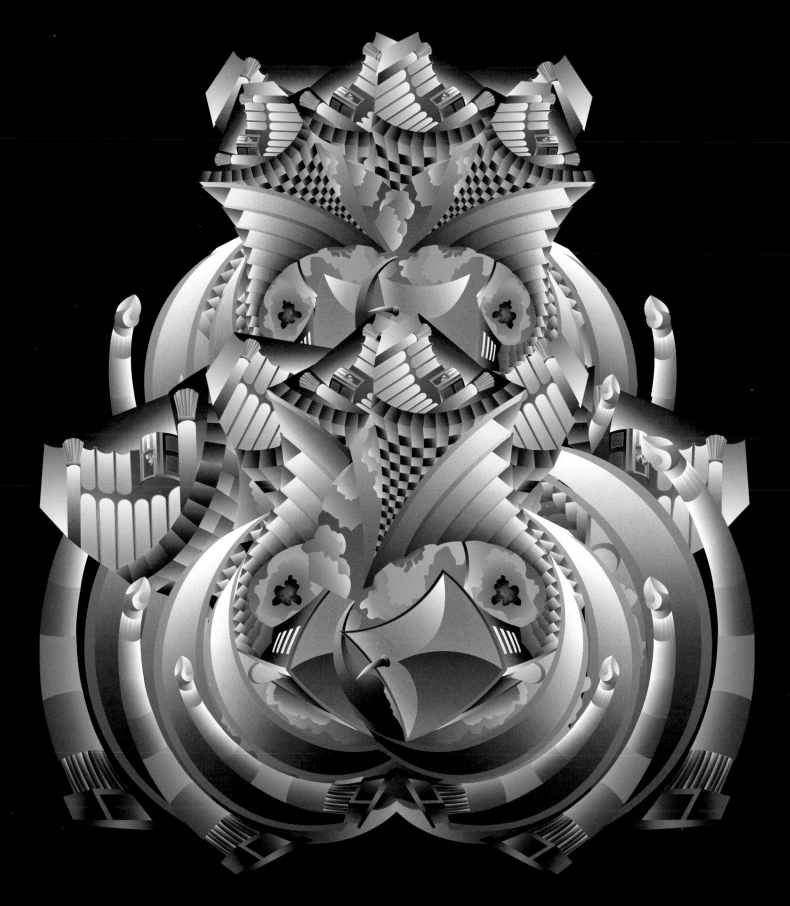

VERY GOOD MOTTOES

THE BANKS OF RIVERS

The two friends followed on the heels of the PM. He kept up a good pace, until they found themselves out of the Maze and once again in the quadrangle.

The quadrangle?

Perhaps it should be referred to as *a* quadrangle, for if it were the same place it was much changed. All wobbly it was, as though it were made of jelly, which, odd as this seemed, did not bother a large crowd which had gathered there. They were interested in something quite different.

There was an air of intense excitement, which made the Puppeteer and Wizkid impatient to know what was happening. Through fleeting gaps in the crowd they pieced together a most extraordinary scene, in which four people wearing costumes resembling a cock, a ram, a lizard and an Old English Sheepdog, were beating upon a Cabinet.

"What on earth are they doing that for?" shouted Wizkid, to make himself heard above the wild cheering of the crowd.

He did not get an answer, but he did attract the attention of some bystanders who, when they saw the PM, began yelling, "Clear a way for the PM and his party! Make way there! Make way!"

A path opened through the crowd and the party was able to take up a position from which they could see clearly what was happening. As though his life depended upon it, Coq was delivering blow after deadly blow upon the Cabinet. Every time his beak smashed onto its target, the PM lost his usual meekness and shouted in a great frenzy, "Go to it! Jolly good swipe! Again!"

In between bouts of shouting encouragement, the PM explained to the young people, "Coq is my Minister for Rousing, he knows all about rousing, he does. A fine fellow! One of the best, although he's a bit wild at present because he ate a whole parrot for lunch and it's turning over in his poor tummy."

"What exactly does he do, apart from beating the guts out of Cabinets and gorging himself silly?" yelled Wizkid.

"His job is to see that everyone is properly roused. A very important job it is too, because if people are badly roused it can lead to no end of discontent; no end of discontent it can lead to."

The PM nodded vigorously in agreement with himself.

"Though I must say what Coq really likes doing, is hitching a lift on passing jet aircraft, being the highly skilled surfer that he is."

"I don't see the connection."

"He doesn't connect, no, he sort of stands on the wings; rather like standing on a surfboard, if you get my drift. Drifts out to sea then surfs back on the aircraft's wings...a very athletic chap, very athletic he is!"

In response to the near toppling of the Cabinet, the cheering rose to an even higher pitch. For a time speech became impossible.

When the noise moderated, the PM pointed to a hedge close by and said, "You see that bell over there, well, Coq has borrowed it from his friends. It's a rousing bell, but it's also a tea bell and also an assembly bell and..."

"...and also a fire bell and also an alarm bell and also a sleep bell," interrupted the Puppeteer, who had got into quite a habit of finishing other people's sentences.

"How did you know that?" asked the PM in alarm. "Only a spy would know that."

"Nonsense," retorted the Puppeteer, "I'm no more guilty of being a spy than you are."

"No more guilty perhaps, but you could be less guilty, don't you think?"

The Puppeteer remained silent, so the PM asked her, in a not unfriendly fashion, "Do you more or less surrender, or do I contact ASIO, the CIA and MI5?"

"I suppose, if I have a choice, I would prefer to surrender less, rather than more, although I would rather not surrender at all if it could be avoided."

"Do you know how to surrender less?"

"By pulling myself up by my bootstrap to lessen..."

"Lesson No 1..."	interrupted the PM,
"Lesson No 1:	First you surrender more.
Lesson No 2:	Then you divide by three.
Lesson No 3:	If you wish to surrender even less, you divide by a bigger number.
Lesson No 4:	Of course if you divide by an even bigger number you will probably become free again."

Then as an afterthought he cautioned, "You have to know your S-matrix theory, though."

"It sounds like a good scheme," enthused the Puppeteer.

The PM looked glum and said, "For you, yes, but not so good for me. Everyone is so frightfully clever with computers these days that I seldom manage to send a spy to prison." He heaved a sigh and confessed, "In fact, I have never sent a spy to prison; never ever sent one to prison. And what is more I believe I never shall send a spy to prison."

Suddenly the crowd stopped cheering, causing the PM's last comment to

carry to the far corners of the quadrangle. He came over all embarrassed, lowered his gaze and to cover his confusion, said sheepishly that he thought it must be half-time. "Time for refreshments," he explained in a more self assured tone.

"Terrific," exclaimed the Puppeteer, "are we going to have something nice?"

"We are going to have Cabinet pudding; Cabinet pudding is what we are going to have," he replied wearily, as though that was all he had been eating for the past month.

Whilst they talked, the PM led them to where Coq was standing with his three colleagues, who began bowing and did not stop until the PM greeted them with, "How's the Cabinet beating going?"

"First rate!" "So, so!" and "Badly!" they answered in turn. The fourth wore a Walkman which pumped her so full of sound there was no way she could have joined in the exchange of words.

"Dog is responsible for Silence, she's in the Department of Silence and Segregation," explained the PM, glancing at the Walkman. "I tell her all the state secrets; she's a very reliable young lady."

"But," objected Wizkid, "I'm sure she won't be able to hear them with that thing over her ears."

"All the better if they are to be kept secret, you know."

"Pass around the Cabinet pudding, there's a good chap," directed Coq, nudging one of his colleagues who was able to oblige only with some difficulty, as he held a large money bag in his left hand. Earlier, he had used the bag to beat on the Cabinet but now it simply hindered him.

"Why does he carry that bag everywhere?" asked Wizkid.

"Because he's the Minister for...the Minister for..."

"The Minister for Defence and Expense, Your Honour," said Coq, who was within earshot of the conversation.

"Ha! Yes! He is responsible for...for..."

"For the Defence and Expenses of the Nation," helped out Coq.

"Yes, yes, yes of course. The Minister for Defence and Expense from the More Office; from the More Office he is," emphasised the PM, looking pleased with himself for being so knowledgeable.

"The More Office?"

"Yes, the More and More and More and More and yet More Office."

"But more what?"

"Why more..."

"Have some more pudding," interrupted Coq.

"You must have More Office permission before you can have more, you know," observed the Lizard importantly. "But... seeing we're amongst friends, I'll let it pass this time."

"What is it made of?" asked the Puppeteer, peering boss-eyed at the pudding thrust under her nose.

"It's very good pudding," the PM assured her glumly.

"It's made of dowels, done to a turn, finely chopped chipboard, flaky melamine laminates and luscious polyurethane varnish," explained Ram (called Rom by his friends), spitting out small pieces of dowelling all over the Puppeteer, "and you couldn't ask for a tastier pudding, not even an **Andromeda Ripple** Crunchy Chocy Bar **with Scrumptiously Toasted Mouth-Watering Tropicana Betelnuts** is tastier."

TROPICANA BETELNUTS   INFO

The Betelnut started life in Malaysia. During the 21st Century it was genetically engineered to its present peak of lusciousness. There is nothing particularly Tropicana about the new Betelnut, nor is it really toasted. It's just that the Proprietors thought their prize product would sell better tarted up this way.

As our 22nd Century readers know, the new Betelnut contains the most seductively delicious juice in existence. Once you've tasted it you've got to have more, more and yet more (with More Office permission, of course) otherwise you'll go crazy.

But there's a snag.

The shell of the new Betelnut is the hardest goddam thing in the Universe. Nothing...nothing will crack it, except a best quality (suitably modified) particle collider. Long before this was generally known, the Proprietors bought up, dirt cheap, all the obsolete machines they could lay their hands on, relieving their previous Owners of the drudgery of keeping them bright and shiny (in compliance with a preservation order slapped on them by the World Heritage Commission).

The ex-Owners swore eternal friendship to the Proprietors for saving them from so much thankless labour, that is until the Beteljuice began to flow and the realisation dawned upon the Ex-Owners that their new found friends were not their friends.

"You're very kind but I think I have had enough Cabinet pudding," said the Puppeteer, brushing crumbs of melamine laminate from her clothing.

"We only use the best varnish, British Paints' Marine Varnish, in point of fact," explained the PM trying to sound enthusiastic.

"Eat up everybody!" directed Ram. "It will soon be time to resume the Cabinet beating."

"Should we send her over first?" asked Ram in a loud voice.

The question puzzled the two friends and seemed to give everyone else food for thought.

The PM took advantage of the lull in the conversation to ask, "Who is that Ram?" He pointed in the direction of the last speaker whilst giving Wizkid a searching look.

Coq came to Wizkid's rescue by explaining that Ram was the Minister for Segregation.

"The Minister for Segrewhater?"

"For Segregation. Surely Your Honour remembers giving him the job of segregating those pupils who are to go on to higher segregation?"

"I did? I could've sworn I'd given that job to Dog." The PM seemed to be unsure about the matter and he threw a number of sidelong glances at Ram, making the poor creature twitch with nervousness.

"Right! Have you made up your minds?" demanded the PM with uncharacteristic decisiveness. "Do we send Dog over to the Cabinet to listen or not?"

None of the party answered him, they just looked thoughtfully into space. Then Liz, who had been peering out of his helmet for some time, sauntered towards the two friends. He walked with a lightness that belied the great weight of his Lizard armour, nevertheless Wizkid and the Puppeteer felt a little cowed when the powerful figure stood towering over them.

"Hello, Dearies," he said in a high pitched voice, "I find Cabinet beating far too tiring a game, don't you?"

LIZ is

a crack motorcyclist and many times winner of the Galactic Motorcycle Championships (held on the Planet Neochina situated in the outer regions of the Betelgeuse System). His speciality is riding highly prized bikes of the late 20th and early 21st Centuries.

His hobby is being Minister for Defence and Expense, a post to which he was appointed because of his ability to endure the wearing of armour for long periods, a skill he had picked up as a hoplite foot soldier in the 5th Century B.C. A tear hangs permanently from his right eyelid. It has hung there ever since his boyhood friend fell at the battle of Thermopylae. It was the last battle in which Liz fought and from which he was the only survivor on the Greek side. His friends believe that the tear will remain there until such time as war is banished forevermore.

As Liz spoke he spat out a shower of chipboard fragments and little pieces of dowelling, which fell like snow upon the shoulders of the two friends. He did not seem to be aware of what he was doing, but went on talking in such an amiable way they could not bring themselves to complain.

"If it were not for the Cabinet pudding, I'd have given up the game long ago."

"Does the game have rules?" asked the Puppeteer in an effort to show some interest.

"Not as a rule, except perhaps on Sundays."

The Puppeteer thought, "It doesn't seem to be a very sensible sort of game which only has rules on one day of the week."

"What rules does it have on Sundays?"

"Nobody knows, as no one has ever played the game on Sunday to find out."

"But, you don't play games to find out about the rules, you know, games are played to win."

"Our games aren't like that. We know who'll win, but we don't know the rules until we've played," explained Liz, spitting out an extra large quantity of pudding.

"I see," said the Puppeteer doubtfully. "The aim of the game is to find out about the rules."

No, no, Dearie," Liz objected impatiently. "The aim of the game is to aim a blow at the Cabinet so as to release the door catch; it being jammed and all."

"That's not a very exciting game."

The PM, who had been silent for a while, now entered the conversation..

"No, not very exciting, I suppose, but very useful; very useful indeed." Then a large tear welled up in his right eye and trickled down his face to end up on the floor. "I shed that tear for eight of my colleagues who are locked up in that there Cabinet."

As though the tear were a signal, everyone began shouting excitedly that Dog should be sent to listen for any sound coming from the Cabinet.

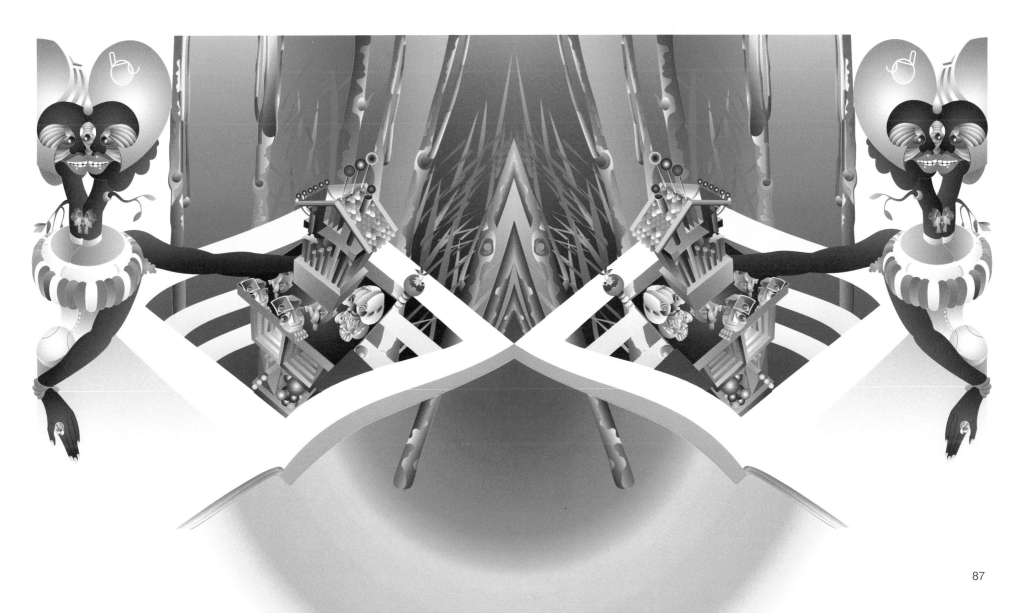

"Why don't you send one of the others," proposed Wizkid, as he watched Dog jive across to the Cabinet, "because," he went on, "she is unlikely to hear anyone with that contraption clamped to her ears."

Looking hurt, the PM explained that his Ministers were extraordinarily sensitive and that any cries coming from inside the Cabinet would upset them no end. "That's why we've sent Dog."

"How long have your colleagues been trapped in the Cabinet?" asked the Puppeteer with concern.

The PM took a TEIKO mk. 2201 Nucleon Chronometer from one of his pockets, peered at it short-sightedly and read off,

"7 years
6 months
5 days
4 hours
3 minutes
2 seconds
10 jiffies
100 milliseconds
10 000 microseconds
1 000 000 nanoseconds
100 000 000 picoseconds
10 000 000 000 chronons,

or it might be a couple of chronons more, because I think the chronometer's running a bit slow."

"Why, that's terrible! They must be desperately hungry and thirsty!" exclaimed the Puppeteer, in horror.

"Only at first," informed the PM gravely. "At first their cries for **Andromeda Ripple Crunchy Chocy Bar with Scrumptiously Toasted Mouth-Watering Tropicana Betelnuts** washed down with lashings of Moet et Chandon Champagne were heart rending, but after a few weeks they seemed to come to terms with their lot and they have been good and quiet ever since. Excellent chaps they are...each and every one of them has a very promising career before him; a very promising career indeed."

He shook his head sadly and then made off, mumbling as he went, "Coq will be ringing the bell shortly for the game to restart so I must make haste; make haste I must."

The Puppeteer was thinking, "If they have promising careers before them, I wouldn't give much for their chances," when her thoughts were interrupted by Liz.

"Do have some of this Cabinet pudding before it gets tarnished, My Dear."

"I don't know how you can eat pudding while your friends are trapped in the Cabinet."

"Deary me, you do invent the easiest conundrums," observed Liz, giving the Puppeteer a pitying look. "Now if you had said, 'I don't know how you could eat pudding while standing upside down with your head in a bucket of souvenirs', well then, I should have had to change the subject, Darling."

Wizkid was about to say something but before he could do so, Liz came in with, "Anyway, My Dears, they're not my friends, they're my colleagues. Yes, Dearies, there are people who find having their colleagues locked away in Cabinets, no end of a handicap. But not to worry, Darlings...yours truly has a lovely talent, because it does not hinder him a tiny bit, no matter what he gets up to. Why only..."

"Look, Dog's returning!" shouted Wizkid. "But the grass, the grass under Dog has turned to glass, into a sheet of glass. She's jiving on a sheet of glass!"

INFO

No, Dog is not jiving on glass, but on an interface between two spacetime zones which she has conjured out of superspace to serve as a pretty backdrop to the little party piece that she is about to enact.

Apart from being an eminent segregationist, Dog is a distinguished member of the Magic Circle, where she is held in the highest regard for the breathtaking originality of the tricks she performs.

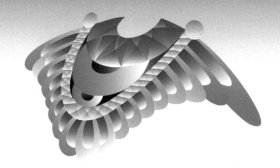

Bathed in an aurora of astral radiance dredged from the depths of superspace, Dog exploded first into one and then into four sets of virtual twins. They shone and shimmered and shook to the sound of...yes...none other than the Superrockets beamed in from goodness knows where! The spectacular appearance of the group sent the crowd wild. Thunderous clapping filled the quadrangle as the glittering chorus of Dogs made its way, writhing and jiving to where the PM was standing on terra firma. For a while the PM was lost to view, amidst a flailing scrum of cloned limbs. Then the clapping stopped. The party piece was over. Dog was yapping away at the PM as though nothing unusual had taken place, her virtual selves, shelved, so to speak.

Liz made no attempt to join Dog and the PM, so Wizkid asked him why he was showing so little interest in what Dog had to report and wasn't that one hell of a stunt to perform in the full light of day.

"It's such a bore, my dears, Dog can only speak Aramaic and as for her tricks they are nothing to what the PM gets up to. You'll see any minute now, the PM will stand on his head and start waving his arms about in a most ridiculous fashion."

"Does he know sign language then?" asked Wizkid.

"Not that beauty, Dearie."

"Wouldn't it be better if someone who did know sign language were to speak to Dog, only knowing Aramaic as she does?"

"What a joy it is to be well segregated," said Liz, mockingly. "No, My Dears, it would not be better."

"I don't see..."

"Because, Sweetie, Dog doesn't know a word of sign language either."

"Then why is the PM acting so queerly?" asked the Puppeteer, as she watched him doing just as Liz said he would.

"Tut, tut, tut, we do ask some questions, don't we?" said Liz, teasingly. "Well, Dearies, he stands on his head and waves his arms about to give him an appetite for the Cabinet pudding which, when he has eaten it, gives him the strength to stand on his head and wave his arms about."

While they were talking the PM had finished his antics and made his way over to the two friends, "Fair takes...your breath...away, that does," he said, panting heavily. "I hope the pudding hasn't tarnished yet," he went on as he helped himself to a hefty portion.

"I have to keep up my strength, you know, so that I can stand on my head and wave my arms about to give me an appetite for..."

A deafening clanging filled the quadrangle. The crowd scattered in all directions, shouting, "Where's the assembly?" and "Where's the fire?" Some of those who remained demanded to know when tea was to be served, whilst others lay upon the grass and fell into a deep sleep.

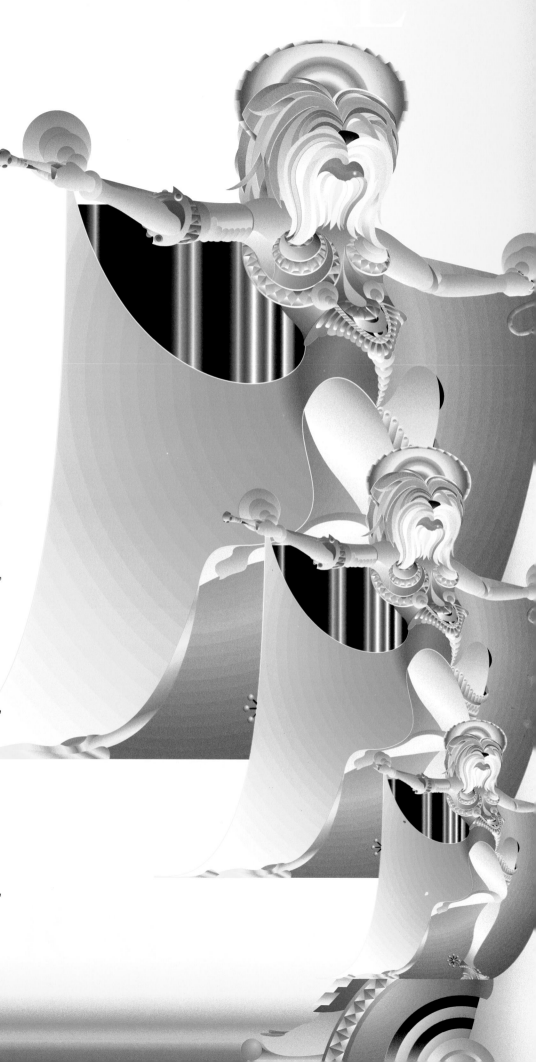

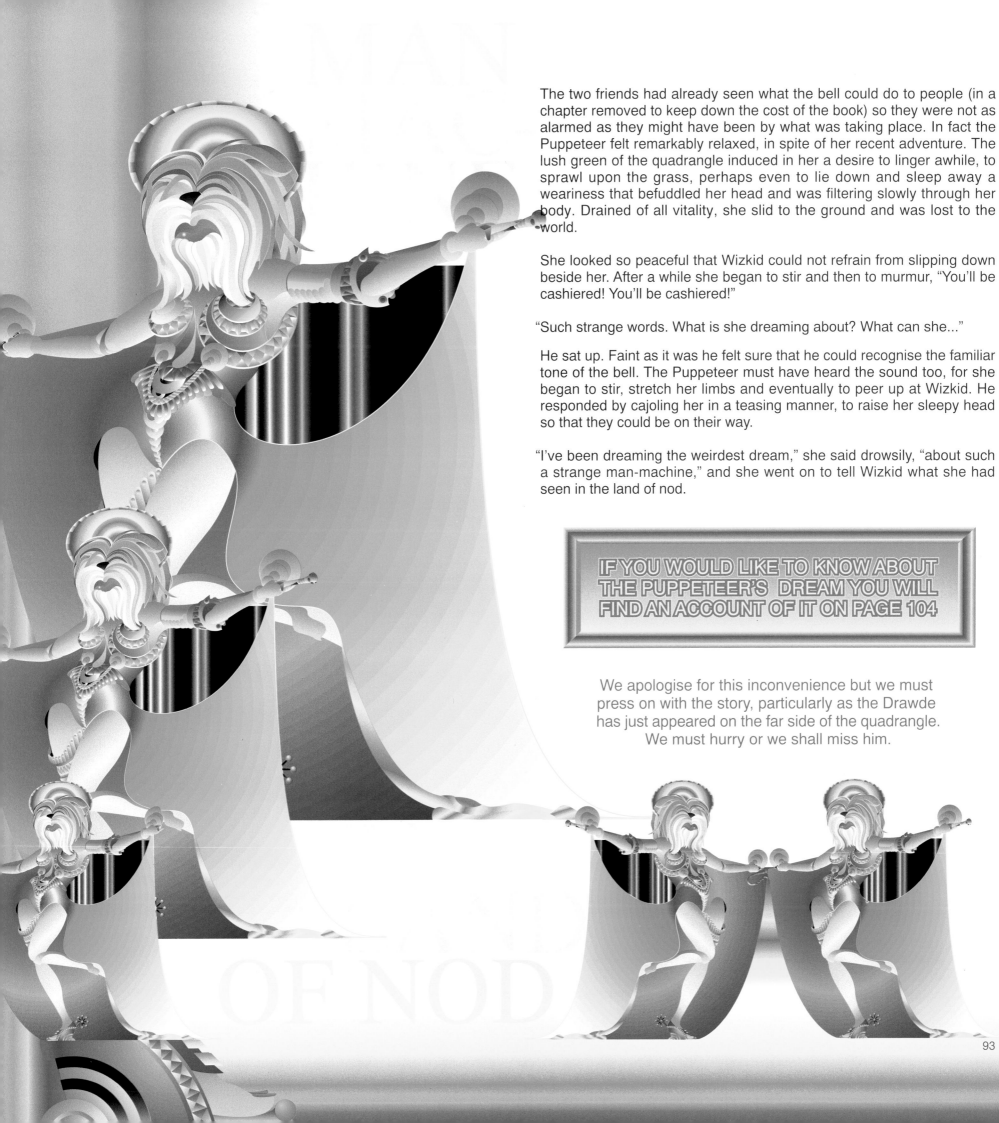

The two friends had already seen what the bell could do to people (in a chapter removed to keep down the cost of the book) so they were not as alarmed as they might have been by what was taking place. In fact the Puppeteer felt remarkably relaxed, in spite of her recent adventure. The lush green of the quadrangle induced in her a desire to linger awhile, to sprawl upon the grass, perhaps even to lie down and sleep away a weariness that befuddled her head and was filtering slowly through her body. Drained of all vitality, she slid to the ground and was lost to the world.

She looked so peaceful that Wizkid could not refrain from slipping down beside her. After a while she began to stir and then to murmur, "You'll be cashiered! You'll be cashiered!"

"Such strange words. What is she dreaming about? What can she..."

He sat up. Faint as it was he felt sure that he could recognise the familiar tone of the bell. The Puppeteer must have heard the sound too, for she began to stir, stretch her limbs and eventually to peer up at Wizkid. He responded by cajoling her in a teasing manner, to raise her sleepy head so that they could be on their way.

"I've been dreaming the weirdest dream," she said drowsily, "about such a strange man-machine," and she went on to tell Wizkid what she had seen in the land of nod.

IF YOU WOULD LIKE TO KNOW ABOUT THE PUPPETEER'S DREAM YOU WILL FIND AN ACCOUNT OF IT ON PAGE 104

We apologise for this inconvenience but we must press on with the story, particularly as the Drawde has just appeared on the far side of the quadrangle. We must hurry or we shall miss him.

THE GENERAL CONFESSES

15

"Come on, hurry! He's heading for the door over there." Wizkid dragged his companion across the quadrangle, ignoring her whinge that she was only half awake.

In spite of their efforts, they were not quick enough to catch the Drawde. In their haste to get through the door, they almost collided with a grand figure of a man who exploded into view between its portals.

"A General, he must be at least a General!" exclaimed the Puppeteer. Her comment was meant for Wizkid's ear alone, but she was so impressed by the magnificence of the person standing before her, that her voice was louder than she intended.

"Actually...actually...I'm not really a General, it's most kind of you to say so, but..."

"Actually, he's a Dorman," interrupted Wizkid.

"Wrong again, if I were a Dorman I'd be in a corridor and I'm not. I'm in..."

"A door," interrupted the Puppeteer (her talent for finishing other people's sentences had not deserted her) "which makes you a Doorman."

"Right again," agreed the Doorman and added, "but I'm also a Cashier. A Cashier who has eaten a whole Coq which had eaten a whole Parrot and is suffering from rummy tummy."

"Really, you don't look at all like a Cashier, although you do look as though you could have eaten a whole Coq which had eaten a whole Parrot." observed the Puppeteer who, as she spoke, could not take her eyes off the Doorman's vast rummy tummy.

Either the Doorman did not hear the remark or chose to ignore it, because he went on to complain that there was only one thing sadder than being a Cashier and that is being a Cashier with a rummy tummy.

The friends glanced at one another and shrugged their shoulders.

"I was once a General, too," he continued a little more brightly. "Not exactly a General, more like a General Doorman, if you get my meaning." He looked wistful and concluded, "But that was a long time ago."

He heaved a great sigh and then another sigh and he would probably have gone on sighing, if the Puppeteer had not asked why he was no longer a General Doorman.

"I suppose you would call it destiny," he explained, looking solemnly towards heaven. "Destiny," he repeated, "that's what it is."

The two friends waited for him to go on but all he did was repeat the word 'destiny', saying it first in one tone then in another as if to become better acquainted with it.

"But what happened?" asked the Puppeteer impatiently.

"Or injustice, it could have been injustice."

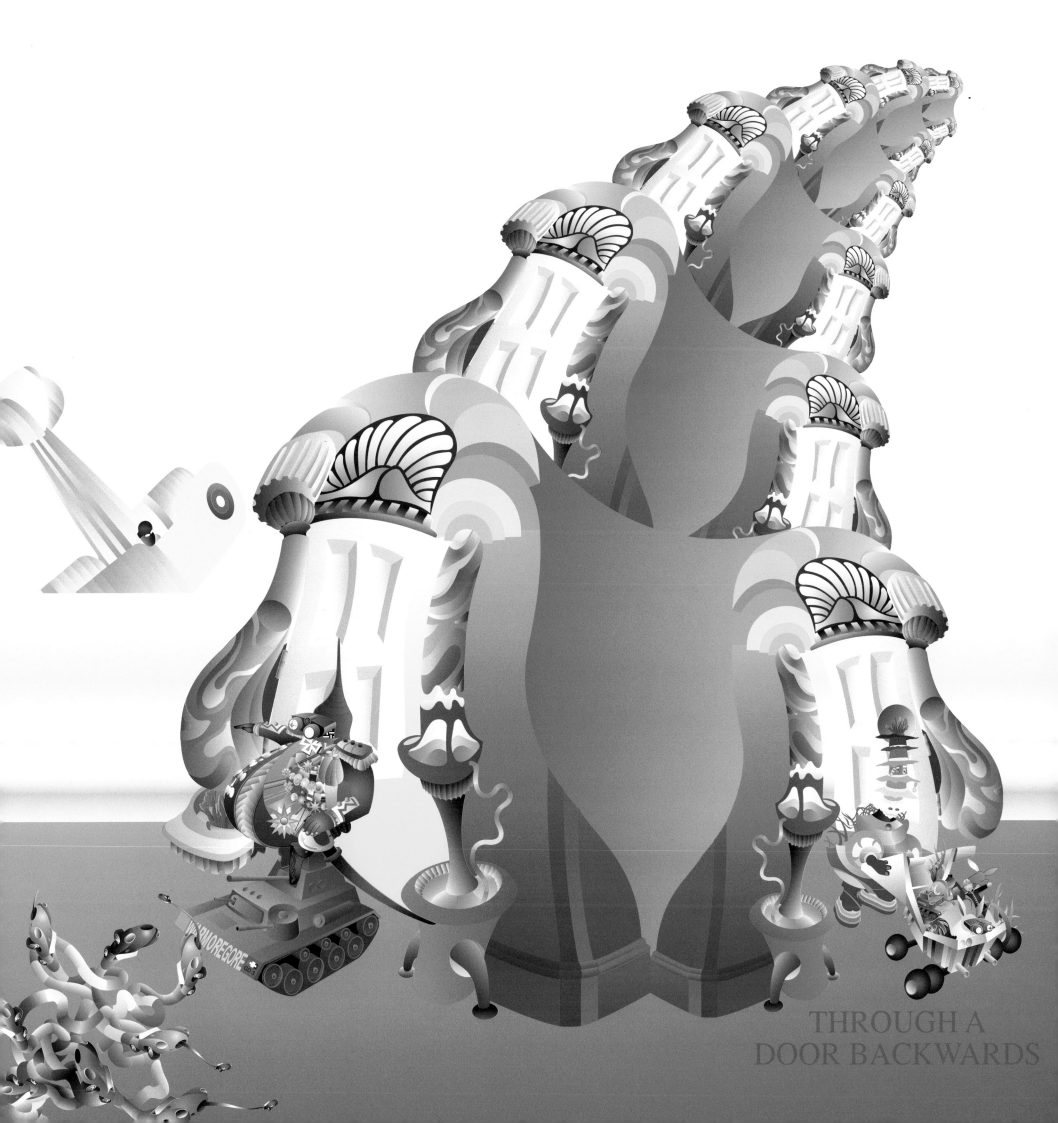

THROUGH A
DOOR BACKWARDS

He repeated 'destiny' and 'injustice' several times, then shook his head sorrowfully and said, "Either way, it was a great tragedy."

"A great tragedy?" queried the Puppeteer, burning with curiosity.

"I've already told you, I was cashiered. How else could I have become a Cashier? Me, a brave...a very brave...a very, very brave hero home from the wars, cashiered!"

The General shook his head and moaned, moaned some more and in between moans, he intoned the words 'destiny', 'injustice' and 'tragedy'.

"But why were you cashiered?" pressed the Puppeteer, not to be sidetracked from a good story.

"I've already told you," he spat out, "because of the cash it was. Why else should I be cashiered?" Then he paused and said, sheepishly, "I didn't take much, either."

"If you didn't take much, then you were treated much too harshly," sympathised the Puppeteer, giving Wizkid a big wink.

"I'd have given back the things I bought with the money, but...but..."

"But what?" asked Wizkid.

"But the planes I bought, crashed," he confessed in a docile voice and then, as though to justify himself, he added, "They *did* crash in the best Art Déco fashion."

"I don't suppose it was your fault at all," said the Puppeteer.

"And ... and the ship sank," he said with his eyes widening.

"You couldn't help it, I'm sure."

"The mansions burnt to the ground," he said with his eyes gleaming.

"These things happen all the time, you know," consoled the Puppeteer.

"And the estates flooded," he said excitedly, with his eyes continuing to widen and gleam in an alarming fashion.

Then his eyes clouded over and he heaved a deep sigh. "Only now I have nothing. Nothing except my uniform that is...they let me keep my uniform."

"I'm glad they let you keep it, because it's a very beautiful uniform," Then she paused and as gently as she could, added, "Except for those brown stains, of course."

"Yes, it's an extremely fine uniform," he agreed, rubbing the rust marks with his sleeve. "Yes, an extremely fine uniform!" he repeated, as he examined a brown stain that had appeared on each of his cuffs.

Then he glared at Wizkid, thrust out a hand and commanded in a sharp

military manner, "And now you must pay me!"

Wizkid was taken unawares. To cover his confusion, he blurted, "Why, because you're a Doorman?"

"Wrong again," said the General. Then he glanced at the Puppeteer as if to say, "Your turn."

"Because you're a Cashier?" she suggested.

"Right again," said the General. "You can't go past a Cashier without paying, you know. It's a very important part of shopping."

"We're not shopping," objected Wizkid.

The General looked suspiciously at the two friends who, in response, shook their heads vigorously.

"I suppose you can prove you're not shopping?"

Neither of them could think of a quick answer, so the General took their hesitation as meaning that they had no proof.

"What, no proof! Not even a certificate, saying for example:

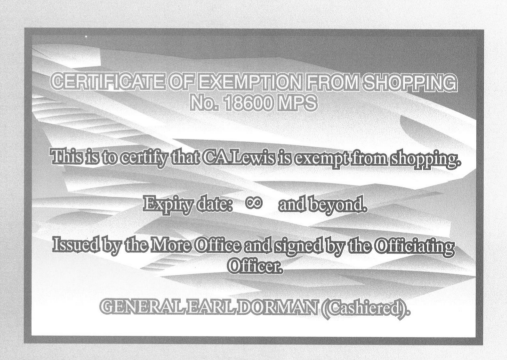

CERTIFICATE OF EXEMPTION FROM SHOPPING
No. 18600 MPS

This is to certify that CA Lewis is exempt from shopping.

Expiry date: ∞ and beyond.

Issued by the More Office and signed by the Officiating Officer.

GENERAL EARL DORMAN (Cashiered).

Of course the wording may be varied this way or that, it's not important, and if you wanted to, you could sign it yourselves."

"I should love to have a certificate like that," said the Puppeteer, eagerly. (She found shopping rather boring, especially what she called 'ordinary shopping'). "Though if we signed it ourselves I don't think it would carry much weight."

EARL DORMAN
In Anglo-Saxon society
an Eardorman or
Ealdorman ranked
second only to the King

THE IN THE BEST
PLANES ART DECO
CRASHED FASHION

YOU SHOULD BE
AS NICE TO
OTHERS AS
THEY ARE TO YOU

YOU MUSTN'T PASS
A DOORMAN
WITHOUT TIPPING
HIM

"Exercise," said the General.

"I beg your pardon," said the Puppeteer.

"Exercise, you must exercise it."

"Exercise what?"

"The certificate, of course," replied the General, impatiently.. "If you want things to carry weight then you must exercise them regularly."

"Where? How?" asked the Puppeteer in bewilderment.

"Where would you expect to exercise a certificate?"

"In a park?" ventured the Puppeteer.

"Whoever heard of a certificate being exercised in a park?" exclaimed the General in a voice full of contempt. "It's not a dog, you know."

"In an exercise book, then?" she suggested hurriedly. "I do all my exercises in an exercise book."

The General frowned and said, "You're not at all the right shape to exercise in a book."

"What she means is that she does her exercises in a book."

The General turned to gaze upon Wizkid, straightened his shoulders, cleared his throat and told the two friends he was given to understand that all sorts of rum things went on in books, "And I don't mind telling you," he explained, "that I prefer not to know about them." He looked fiercely at the Puppeteer and added in a stern voice, "Stay clear of them is my advice, if you want to stay healthy."

She nodded half-heartedly, wishing dearly that he would talk about something nice.

"Which brings us back full circle to the business in hand," said the General, "not that you've put anything into my hand as yet."

He had held his palm open all the time he had been talking. Now he put it right under Wizkid's nose in a most embarrassing fashion and said in a threatening voice, "Now you must pay!"

"But, we only want to go through the door."

"Now you must pay," repeated the General and he thrust his hand so hard under Wizkid's nose that the poor boy had to stand on tiptoe to carry on breathing.

"Why? Because you're a Cashier?" (Wizkid was playing for time in the hope that things would take a turn for the better).

"Wrong again," snapped the General.

"Because you're a Doorman?" suggested the Puppeteer.

"Right again, YOU MUSTN'T PASS A DOORMAN WITHOUT TIPPING HIM, you know. It's the second law of etiquette."

"Excuse me for asking, sir," she said humbly, "if that is the second law of etiquette, what is the first law?"

The General was so charmed by the Puppeteer's manner that he allowed his palm to drop from under Wizkid's nose. At the same time he gave her a broad smile and said, "MIND YOUR OWN BUSINESS."

"You should be as nice to others as they are to you," objected Wizkid angrily.

"Wrong again," said the General. "YOU SHOULD BE AS NICE TO OTHERS AS THEY ARE TO YOU, is the third law of etiquette. The first law is, MIND YOUR OWN BUSINESS."

"And what is the fourth law, sir?" asked the Puppeteer.

"NEVER JUMP TO CONCLUSIONS ."

"And the fifth?"

"Don't ask too many questions."

"That is the fifth law," confirmed Wizkid, anxious to get something right for once.

"Wrong again - the fifth law of etiquette is, ALWAYS TRY TO GET THINGS RIGHT. "

"You've just invented those laws," objected Wizkid peevishly.

"I thought you'd never notice," declared the General, preening himself, "you may congratulate me, if you wish."

"It's not fair to invent laws whenever it suits you."

"Fair, dark or mousy, it makes no odds," said the Doorman in a superior fashion. "This here doorway, the quadrangle, that there maze, everything in the world and a great deal outside it has been invented at sometime or other. You've invented me, I've invented you, we've invented her and she's invented both of us."

"You've just invented that too," grumbled Wizkid.

"Right again...and that's enough etymology for the moment...have you decided how much you are going to tip me?"

"Tips," declared Wizkid emphatically, "are only given to people who are helpful."

"People are only helpful when they are given tips."

Wizkid is showing his ignorance. Had he been briefed before entering the Maze, he might have been more open-minded, for he would have learned that there is no law about laws being changed.

The Ten Dimensional Maze is programmed to enable you to apply new laws to anything you fancy. Apart from the laws/rules of etiquette, Ten Dimensional Cricket, etc., you coul, for example, punch out new laws of physics and create a universe in which time runs backwards, or in which there are any number of space dimensions up to nine. In fact you could put together an 'infinity' of space-time scenarios and enjoy the KALUZA KLEIN KALEIDOSCOPIC KOSMIC KONSEQUENCES. Of course any new cosmic order that you happen upon, is programmed to remain in the realm of Superreality, otherwise you could programme out of existence:

me

you

the World

the Solar System

the Universe as we know and don't know it

EVERYTHING

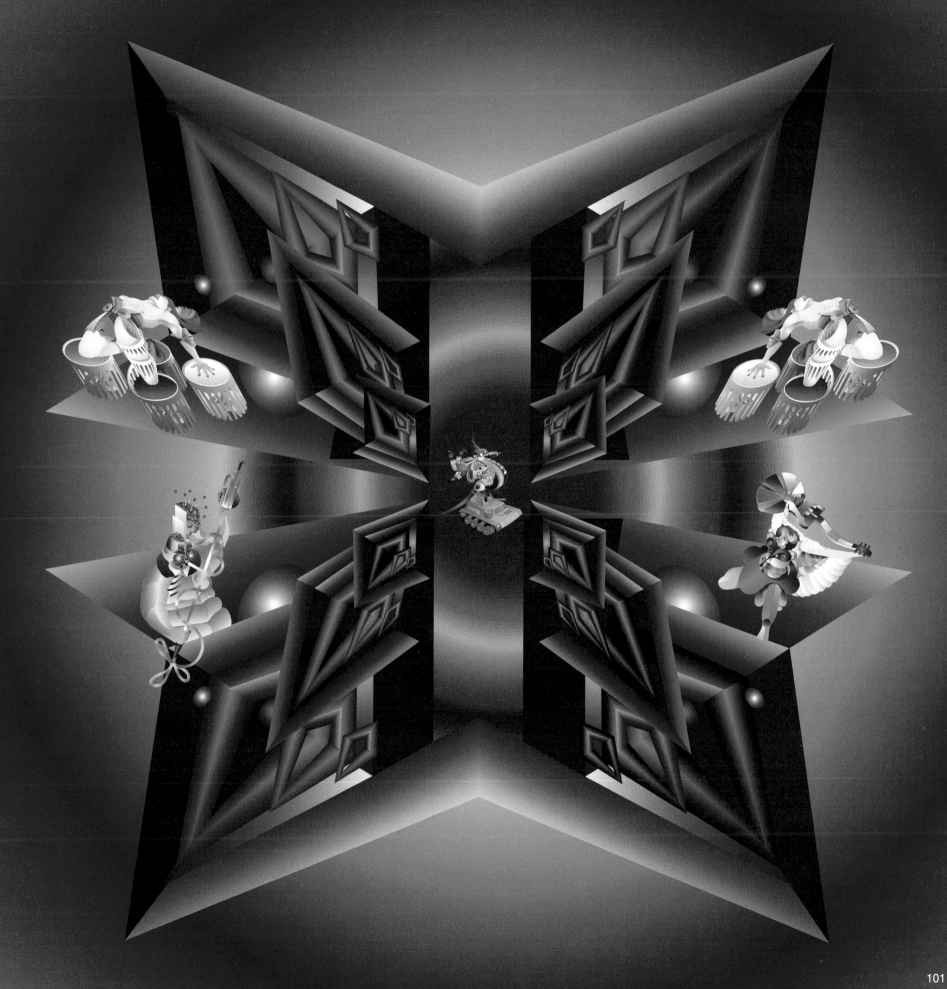

"Would tuppence be enough, sir?" interceded the Puppeteer.

"Tuppence! **TUPPENCE!**" thundered the Doorman. "**ME**...**GENERAL DOORMAN** (cashiered), man of destiny...**ME**...with connections in the best corridors and doorways, being offered tuppence, **TUPPENCE!** You couldn't make that **three** pence by any chance, could you?"

"I only have tuppence, sir."

"Only tuppence, you say. Hmmm ... an IOU perhaps? You could give me an IOU for the extra penny."

"That's stingy," objected Wizkid.

"Right again," agreed the General and he turned to the Puppeteer and said, "You'd better make out that there IOU for eleven pence."

"That's not what I meant."

"Not eleven pence," murmured the General, puzzling over what Wizkid had said. Then his eyes lit up and he exclaimed, "Yes...by golly, you are an artist, Sir! A true artist! It's an ugly amount...all sort of hanging to one side." He paused to consider a moment and added enthusiastically, "What we need is a nice round figure."

Through half closed eyes the General peered into space and recited sums of money that grew larger and larger. By the time he had got to a grand, Wizkid had become thoroughly alarmed.

"I think a grand is a very attractive figure," Wizkid proclaimed hastily, in an attempt to head off the General.

"You do?"

"Yes, very attractive."

"Compact and nicely rounded, would you say? Not ashamed to take it anywhere?"

"Just the job."

"You don't think an additional amount would...would..."

"Vulgar - terribly vulgar."

"Hmmm," murmured the General pensively, "surely just a touch of vulgarity... would...would..."

"Spoil everything."

"Hmmm..."

"But, sir..." said the Puppeteer.

"What is it, Girl?"

"I don't have any paper to write the IOU on."

"What IOU?".

"**The** IOU, Sir."

"The IOU," mimicked the General. "The IOU... to be sure, the IOU... for ten grand, wasn't it?"

"It was not," objected Wizkid vehemently.

"It was not? Then it must have been for twenty grand."

"No..." began Wizkid.

"Yes!" exclaimed the General excitedly. "Everything is coming back to me...as clear as day...twenty glorious grand. Forty round, plump, luscious grand was the sum agreed to." As he spoke he turned his back on Wizkid's protestations and addressed the Puppeteer.

"No paper, you say...no paper?" He patted the pockets of his uniform. A sound like dry leaves came from inside his tunic. The General put his hand into his breast pocket and drew out an ancient leaf of golden yellow parchment.

"Just the thingumajig for the job," he said, handing it to the Puppeteer.

With a stub of pencil thrust into her hand by the General, she worked away at the parchment. It was not an easy task because she had to write extremely carefully to prevent the ancient material from crumbling.

The moment she had finished, the General greedily snatched the IOU from her hand. This was too much for the fragile parchment for it crumbled into pieces. As they fell to the ground in a shower of worthless gold, the General gave a frantic cry and stooped, but before he could lay his hands on the 'treasure' it was whipped away by a gust of wind.

With a deafening noise the tank shuddered into life. The tracks creaked and screeched as it rolled across the quadrangle, carrying the General in hot pursuit of the pieces of golden parchment.

THE FIVE LAWS OF ETIQUETTE
According to General Earl Dorman

1. Mind your own business.
2. You mustn't pass a Doorman without tipping him.
3. You should be as nice to others as they are to you.
4. Never jump to conclusions.
5. Always try to get things right.

THE PUPPETEER'S

She was looking into a mirror in which was reflected the image of a quadrangle, where a military man, mounted on a tank, was rampaging back and forth, chasing what appeared to be a shower of gold. Because of the tank's poor manoeuvrability, the treasure always managed to stay ahead of its pursuer. Earth, grass and shrubs flew through the air, as the vehicle's tracks wrought destruction on all that lay in their path.

As the Puppeteer watched, she saw the scene before her transform from a thing of beauty, into a devastated landscape of gaping craters, ugly mounds and mud.

Then she heard a camera shutter click and the image flipped. The quadrangle was again a thing of beauty, a changed, strange beauty of light without source. Undulating, sometimes hovering structures, were set against unfathomable space and teetered at the margins of a fragmented quadrangle. The man/machine was gone, instead there was a boy. He was playing with a toy tank and imagining a great battle, in which implacable enemies were locked in a struggle to the death.

"You'll be cashiered...you'll be cashiered," she heard herself shout, as once again the shutter clicked, and once again she looked upon the devastated landscape. The fearsome duo was no longer in sight and yet there was a pile of mud that had a certain military look about its contours, until it expired with a plop, into a slurry of its own creation.

DREAM 16

KOOGY STOPS READING

The two friends stood alone in the quadrangle. The General had gone. The PM and his ministers had long gone. Silence reigned. A feeling of solitude swept over Wizkid. He looked soulfully at the Puppeteer and saw her, as though for the first time; the wistful light in her clear eyes; her beautiful black skin; the deep rich chiaroscuro of her dark hair; everything. She responded by moving closer to her companion and sneaked her hand in his.

Something must have disturbed her for she suddenly withdrew from Wizkid, gave a little cry and stared desperately ahead of her.

"Whatever is the matter?" asked Wizkid.

"We must warn them,", answered the Puppeteer.

"Warn who?"

"The two friends.".

"Who?"

"Before Koogy closes the book.".

"What book?"

"Don't you see?"

"What?"

"It's the end... THE END.".

Koogy was forced to break off, because the Puppeteer complained she had not understood a single word of the last bit of the story and that it was worse gibberish than the Gobbledygook's nonsense.

"Don't worry, Guys," exhorted Koogy. "It's a virus. A virus must have gotten into the program and that dummy of an Author hasn't had the savvy to edit it out of the book."

"I am sorry because I do like to hear stories right to the end, especially when they have happy endings."

Koogy let the open page go. Instead of the rustle of paper, the friends heard the metallic clunk of an Audi Quartz car door being slammed. Taken unawares, Wizkid started back. He barely had time to recover his composure when the sound of an engine being revved filled the air. The two friends darted anxious glances around them, fully expecting to have to jump for their very lives to avoid the oncoming rush of a bundle of German automotive technology. The sound continued unabated in spite of there being no sign of the car itself. After several surges of power, the sound of the phantom engine finally faded away and in its wake a new sound was heard...the disembodied voice of a recorded message.

"ADJUST YOUR REAR VIEW MIRROR. FASTEN YOUR SEAT-BELTS. DECIDE ON YOUR DESTINATION AND PROCEED CAREFULLY. YOU ARE IN CHARGE."

"There you are...that proves it." Wizkid pounced on the mechanical utterance like a tiger taking its prey. "We're the ones who decide where we go, not that precious Author of yours, and as for that claptrap about viruses..."

"You're right, you're right...I guess you're right," agreed Koogy uncertainly. "Nilrem knows...he has the answer. Didn't I tell you the way...way back there...the way to Nilrem?"

"The way to the PM, not to Nilrem," corrected Wizkid.

"Yeah, don't you see...the PM laid it on the line. Remember all that stuff about clear rivers running with fish, clean streets, beautiful houses and the sun always shining in pollution-free skies? You know, the well mannered map? The PM can't do it, but Nilrem...he can unfold it." As she spoke, Koogy leaned across the invisible table to close the book. "You must help...that's where you can play a role. Nilrem can't do it alone. WE MUST ALL HELP."

"That's all very well but I don't call this a happy ending," objected the Puppeteer, putting out a hand to prevent the book being closed. "Why can't we...?"

Her protest was cut short as the pages came together with a resounding thud.

THE SHOWMAN'S LAMENT

MY LORDS, LADIES AND GENTLEMEN, THE PROPRIETORS ARE DEEPLY DISSATISFIED.

THEY HAVE INSTRUCTED ME TO COMMISERATE WITH YOU, DEAR READERS, FOR HAVING UNCOMPLAININGLY ENDURED THIS TALE, WHICH, IN SPITE OF THE MANY INTERVENTIONS OF YOUR HUMBLE SERVANT, LEAVES MUCH TO BE DESIRED. NOTWITHSTANDING THEIR PROFOUND DISAPPOINTMENT, THE PROPRIETORS HAVE GRACIOUSLY CONDESCENDED NOT TO BELABOUR ITS MANY FAULTS BUT TO SAY SIMPLY THAT IT HAS FALLEN WELL BELOW THEIR MODEST EXPECTATIONS.

THEY FEEL MOST STRONGLY THAT YOU, OUR STAUNCH AND LOYAL READERS, HAVING UNSTINTINGLY INVESTED SO MUCH OF YOUR VALUABLE TIME IN LOYALLY READING THE BOOK RIGHT TO THE VERY END, SHOULD BE LEFT WITH AN OVERWHELMING, A RESOUNDING SENSE OF A COMING TOGETHER OF PARTS, A TYING OF LOOSE ENDS, A JOB WELL DONE.

INSTEAD, THE PROPRIETORS PERCEIVE A TALE FALTERING, NAY LIMPING, TO AN INDECISIVE AND INGLORIOUS FINALE.

THEREFORE, ON BEHALF OF YOUR GOODSELVES, OUR PATIENT READERS, THE PROPRIETORS HAVE INSTRUCTED ME TO REQUEST, IN FACT TO DEMAND, THAT THE AUTHOR REDEEM HIMSELF IN SOME SMALL MEASURE BY PROVIDING US ALL WITH A SATISFACTORY ACCOUNT OF THE FOLLOWING UNRESOLVED MATTERS:

WHO IS NILREM?

WHY IS THE PUPPETEER ALWAYS WINK-ING AT WIZKID? (AND SURELY SHE HAS A PROPER NAME LIKE THE REST OF US?)

WHAT HAPPENED TO THE MAZE?

WHO IS NILREM?

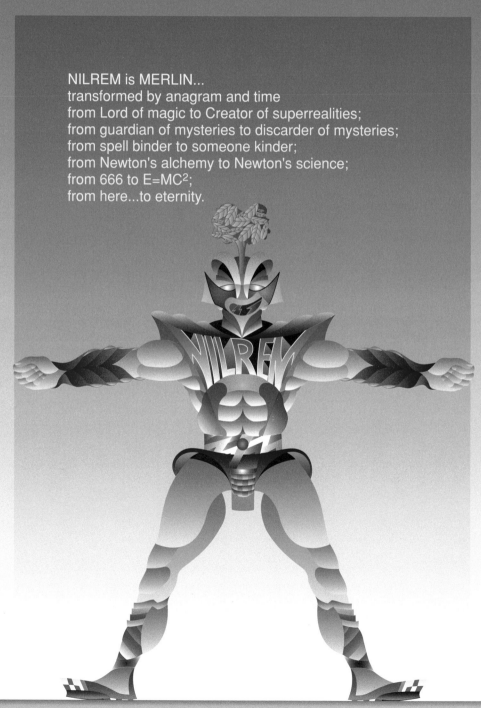

NILREM is MERLIN...
transformed by anagram and time
from Lord of magic to Creator of superrealities;
from guardian of mysteries to discarder of mysteries;
from spell binder to someone kinder;
from Newton's alchemy to Newton's science;
from 666 to $E=MC^2$;
from here...to eternity.

THE PUPPETEER

For those readers who, like the Proprietors, have not already guessed, her name is, of course, Carol...Carol Lewis...more precisely, Carol A. Lewis. And the 'A'? It stands for Ariadne, after the young lady who helped Theseus find his way through the Labyrinth (Maze).

The Showman asks why she winks at Wizkid so often?

Now that is a puzzle!

Perhaps it has something to do with the fact that a Puppeteer's job is to pull strings?

WHAT HAPPENED TO THE MAZE?

IT VANISHED.

Vamoosed at the precise moment an announcement was made by the Head of Project Nutcracker (University of New Shanghai, on the planet Neochina) that their brand new super colossal Titan Whirlitron Collider had proven that the Ten Dimensional Maze is impossible. That Superstrings do not exist because monopoles... whatever they are...do not exist, because a couple of other things... whatever they are...do not exist and that, given more time, they would be able to prove that nothing at all exists, not even the super colossal Titan Whirlitron Collider.

Two days later the Proprietors went on record saying that their Superstring Wizkid was onto something really big and that it would not be long before the Ten Dimensional Maze would once again adorn the quadrangle.

Since then word has come in from time to time about this person or that person having seen the Maze but so far the reports have remained unconfirmed.

So is it the end of the the Ten Dimensional Maze?

Well, not quite...because of the PM. Nobody told him about the Maze vanishing. He still haunts its ghostly paths. Round and round he trudges, murmuring his school mottoes, and lamenting that he will never ever get to see the Big Apple.

NILREM IS EVERYWHERE

MERLIN

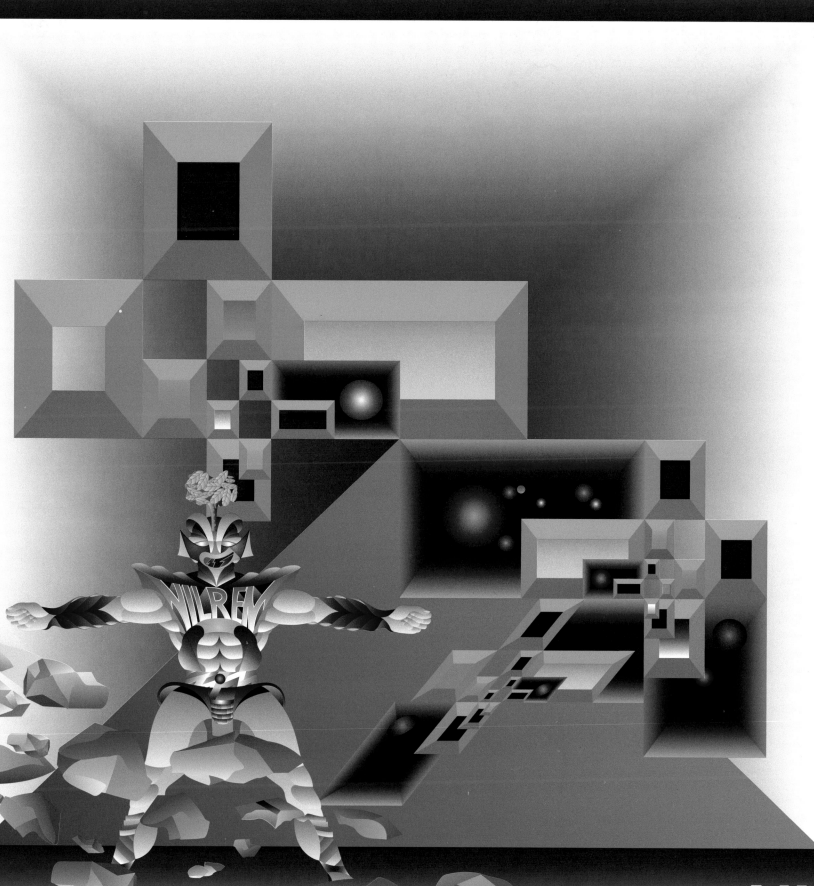

NILREM